The
Supporters'
Guide
to
Premier &
Football League
Clubs
2018

EDITOR
John Robinson

Thirty-fourth Edition

CONTENTS

British Library Cataloguing in Publication Data
A catalogue record for this book is available from the British Library

ISBN: 978-1-86223-356-0

Copyright © 2017, SOCCER BOOKS LIMITED (01472 696226)
72 St. Peter's Avenue, Cleethorpes, N.E. Lincolnshire, DN35 8HU, England
Web site   www.soccer-books.co.uk
e-mail   info@soccer-books.co.uk

Manufactured in the UK by T.J. International of Padstow.

FOREWORD

We are indebted to the staffs of all the clubs featured in this guide for their cooperation and also to Michael Robinson (page layouts), Bob Budd (cover artwork) and Tony Brown (Cup Statistics – www.soccerdata.com). Also, we wish to thank Sheffield Wednesday and Wolverhampton Wanderers for providing photographs used on the front cover.

When using this guide, please note that concessions also include senior citizens unless stated otherwise. Some clubs (particularly those which were promoted at the end of the 2016/2017 season) had not fixed their matchday admission prices for 2017/2018 at the time of going to press and in these cases we have been unable to include current admission information. It should be noted that although actual matchday admission prices are shown in this guide, prices can vary and although many clubs offer discounts for tickets purchased before the day of the game, some prices may be higher than those stated. There is also a move towards variable 'demand-based' pricing at certain clubs.

Disabled Supporters' information is once again included in the guide and, to ensure that facilities are not overstretched, we recommend that fans with disabilities pre-book wherever possible.

Regular purchasers of the guide will notice that we have included a number of new ground photographs in this edition. Ground redevelopment is continuing apace and travelling fans may find that away sections and prices change during the course of the 2017/2018 season.

If any readers have alternative ground photos which they would like us to consider for insertion in future issues, they should write to me care of the address opposite.

Finally, we would like to wish our readers a happy and safe spectating season.

John Robinson
EDITOR

WEMBLEY STADIUM

First Opened: 1923 (Re-opened in 2007 after rebuild)
Address: Wembley National Stadium, Wembley, London HA9 0WS
Correspondence: P.O. Box 1966, London, SW1P 3EQ
Telephone Nº: 0844 980-8001
Fax Number: (020) 8795-5050

Seating Capacity: 90,000 over three tiers –
Lower Tier: 34,303 seats
Middle Tier: 16,532 seats
Upper Tier: 39,165 seats
Web site: www.wembleystadium.com

GENERAL INFORMATION

Car Parking: The stadium is a Public Transport Location and, as such, parking is only available for pre-accredited vehicles. Any spaces which are available must be pre-purchased from the following web site: www.wembleyofficialparking.com
Coach Travel: National Express operates coach routes from hundreds of towns and cities direct to the stadium for special events: www.nationalexpress.com/wembley
Rail & Tube Travel: Wembley Park station is on the Jubilee and Metropolitan tube lines; Wembley Stadium station is on the Chiltern mainline and Wembley Central station is served by the Bakerloo tube, London Overground and London Midland and Southern railway lines.
Local Bus Services: Services 18, 83, 92, 182, 223 and 483 all travel to the stadium

FANS WITH DISABILITIES INFORMATION

Wheelchairs: 310 spaces for wheelchairs are available in total alongside 310 seats for helpers. A further 100 enhanced amenity seats are available for ambulant visitors.
Disabled Toilets: Available throughout the stadium.

ACCRINGTON STANLEY FC

Founded: 1876 (Reformed 1968)
Former Names: None
Nickname: 'Stanley' 'Reds'
Ground: Wham Stadium, Livingstone Road, Accrington, Lancashire   BB5 5BX
Record Attendance: 4,386 (7th May 2016)
Pitch Size: 112 × 72 yards

Colours: Red shirts and shorts
Telephone Nº: (01254) 356950
Fax Number: (01254) 356951
Ground Capacity: 5,070
Seating Capacity: 2,000
Web site: www.accringtonstanley.co.uk
E-mail: info@accringtonstanley.co.uk

GENERAL INFORMATION

Car Parking: Street parking only
Coach Parking: Livingstone Road near the Away entrance
Nearest Railway Station: Accrington (1 mile)
Nearest Bus Station: Accrington Town Centre (1 mile)
Club Shop: At the ground and through the club web site
Opening Times: Weekdays 10.00am – 4.00pm; Saturday matchdays 10.00am – 5.00pm
Telephone Nº: (01254) 356950

GROUND INFORMATION

Away Supporters' Entrances & Sections:
Signposted on matchdays

ADMISSION INFO (2017/2018 PRICES)

Adult Standing: £20.00
Adult Seating: £20.00
Senior Citizen Standing: £15.00
Senior Citizen Seating: £15.00
Ages 12-16 Standing/Seating: £10.00
Under-12s Standing/Seating: £5.00
Programme Price: £3.00

FANS WITH DISABILITIES INFORMATION

Wheelchairs: Specific areas around the ground
Helpers: Admitted
Prices: Concessionary prices are charged for both fans with disabilities and their helpers
Disabled Toilets: Available
Contact: (01254) 356950   Robert Houseman, Disabled Liaison Officer (Bookings are necessary)

Travelling Supporters' Information:
Routes: Take the M6 to the M65 signposted for Blackburn/Burnley. Exit at Junction 7 and follow the sign for Padiham. Turn right at first traffic lights then right at next. Follow Whalley Road towards Accrington, go through lights at the Greyhound Inn. Turn left into Livingstone Road, 500 yards past traffic lights (signposted Accrington Stanley). The ground is signposted from Junction 7 of the M65 – follow the brown signs with the white football.

AFC BOURNEMOUTH

Founded: 1899 (**Entered League**: 1923)
Former Names: Boscombe FC (1899-1923);
Bournemouth & Boscombe Athletic FC (1923-1972)
Nickname: 'Cherries'
Ground: Vitality Stadium, Dean Court,
Bournemouth, Dorset   BH7 7AF
Ground Capacity: 11,464 (All seats)

Record Attendance: 11,772 (21st July 2013)
Pitch Size: 115 × 74 yards
Colours: Red & Black striped shirts with Black shorts
Telephone Nº & Ticket Office Nº: 0344 576-1910
Fax Number: (01202) 726373
Web Site: www.afcb.co.uk
E-mail: enquiries@afcb.co.uk

GENERAL INFORMATION
Car Parking: Car Park for 200 cars behind the ground
Coach Parking: At the ground
Nearest Railway Station: Bournemouth Central (1½ miles)
Nearest Bus Stop: Holdenhurst Road, Bournemouth
Club Shop: At the ground
Opening Times: Monday to Friday 9.00am to 5.00pm,
Saturday 9.30am to 4.00pm, Sunday 11.00am to 3.00pm and
Saturday Matchdays 9.00am to kick-off.
Telephone Nº: 0844 576 -1910

GROUND INFORMATION
Away Supporters' Entrances & Sections:
East Stand turnstiles 'F' 14-16 for East Stand accommodation

ADMISSION INFO (2017/2018 PRICES)
Adult Seating: £32.00 – £55.00
Child Seating: £6.00 – £18.00
Concessionary Seating: £19.00 – £40.00
Note: Family tickets are also available. In view of the
limited capacity of Dean Court, most seats for 2015/2016 will
be taken by season ticket holders.

FANS WITH DISABILITIES INFORMATION
Wheelchairs: Spaces available in all stands
Helpers: One carer admitted per fan with disabilities
Prices: £5.00 for those in wheelchairs.
Disabled Toilets: Available in Main, East and North Stands
Contact: 0344 576-1910   (Bookings are necessary)
E-mail Contact: disability@afcb.co.uk

Travelling Supporters' Information: Routes: From the North & East: Take the A338 into Bournemouth and turn left at
'Kings Park' turning. After the slip road go straight forward at the mini-roundabout into Kings Park Drive – a car park is 500 yards
on the left and the ground is nearby; From the West: Head into Bournemouth and join the A338, take the slip road at the
Springbourne Roundabout, signposted for Kings Park. Take the 3rd exit at the roundabout at the fire station, stay in the left-hand
lane and turn left onto Holdenhurst Road. Go straight on at the traffic lights (the Queen's Park Pub should be on the right) and
take the 3rd exit at the mini roundabout into Kings Park for the ground.

AFC WIMBLEDON

Founded: 2002 (**Entered League**: 2011)
Former Names: Originally formed as Wimbledon Old Centrals (1889-1905) who later became Wimbledon FC
Nickname: 'The Dons'
Ground: The Cherry Red Records Fans' Stadium – Kingsmeadow, Jack Goodchild Way, 422A Kingston Road, Kingston-upon-Thames, Surrey   KT1 3PB
Record Attendance: 4,850 (2016)

Pitch Size: 112 × 71 yards
Ground Capacity: 5,027
Seating Capacity: 2,140
Colours: Shirts and Shorts are Blue with Yellow trim
Telephone Nº: (020) 8547-3528
Fax Number: 0808 280-0816
Web site: www.afcwimbledon.co.uk
E-mail: info@afcwimbledon.co.uk

GENERAL INFORMATION

Car Parking: At the ground
Coach Parking: At the ground
Nearest Railway Station: Norbiton (1 mile)
Nearest Bus Station: Kingston
Club Shop: At the ground
Opening Times: Matchdays only
Telephone Nº: (020) 8547-3528

GROUND INFORMATION

Away Supporters' Entrances & Sections:
Turnstiles 9 and 10

ADMISSION INFO (2017/2018 PRICES)

Adult Standing: £17.00 – £20.00
Adult Seating: £24.00 – £29.00
Concessionary Standing: £11.00 – £12.00
Concessionary Seating: £15.00 – £18.00
Under-18s Standing: £4.00 – £5.00
Under-18s Seating: £10.00 – £13.00
Programme Price: £3.00

FANS WITH DISABILITIES INFORMATION

Wheelchairs: Accommodated around the ground
Helpers: Please phone the club for information
Prices: Please phone the club for information
Disabled Toilets: Yes
Contact: (020) 8547-3528   (Bookings are necessary)

Travelling Supporters' Information:
Routes: Exit the M25 at Junction 10 and take the A3 to the New Malden/Worcester Park turn-off and turn into Malden Road (A2043). Follow Malden Road to the mini-roundabout and turn left into Kingston Road. Kingsmeadow is situated approximately 1 mile up the Kingston Road, on the left-hand side and is signposted from the mini-roundabout.

ARSENAL FC

Founded: 1886 **(Entered League**: 1893)
Former Names: Royal Arsenal (1886-1891) and
Woolwich Arsenal (1891-1914)
Nickname: 'Gunners'
Ground: Emirates Stadium, Queensland Road N7
Ground Capacity: 60,272 (All seats)
Pitch Size: 115 × 74 yards
Record Attendance: 60,161 (3rd November 2007)

Colours: Red shirts with White sleeves, White shorts
Telephone Nº: (020) 7619-5003
Ticket Office: 0844 277-3625
Fax Number: (020) 7704-4001
Office Address: Highbury House, 75 Drayton Park,
London N5 1BU
Web Site: www.arsenal.com
E-mail: ask@arsenal.co.uk

GENERAL INFORMATION

Car Parking: None
Coach Parking: Visit the web site for further details
Nearest Railway Station: Finsbury Park and Highbury &
Islington
Nearest Tube Station: Arsenal (Piccadilly), Finsbury Park,
Highbury & Islington and Holloway Road are all nearby
Club Shop: At the ground and at Finsbury Park Tube Station
Opening Times: Monday to Saturday 9.00am to 6.00pm;
Sundays 10.00am to 4.00pm
Telephone Nº: (020) 7619-5003

GROUND INFORMATION

Away Supporters' Entrances & Sections:
Green quadrant – follow colour coding system at the ground

ADMISSION INFO (2017/2018 PRICES)

Adult Seating: £27.00 – £97.00
Child Seating: £10.00 – £32.50 (Members only)
Senior Citizen Seating: £11.25 – £36.50 (Members only)
Note: Prices vary depending on the category of the game.
Concessionary prices are only available to Members.
Programme Price: £3.00

FANS WITH DISABILITIES INFORMATION

Wheelchairs: 250 spaces available in areas throughout the
ground. A similar number of places are available for the
ambulant and visually impaired
Helpers: One helper admitted for each fan with disabilities
Prices: Registered supporters with disabilities are admitted
for half the normal prices. Helpers are admitted free
Disabled Toilets: Many available throughout the ground
Free commentaries are available for the visually impaired
Contact: (020) 7619-5050   (Bookings are necessary)

Travelling Supporters' Information:
As the stadium is situated in a mainly residential area, only car owners with resident's permits will be allowed to park in the
designated on-street parking areas. Cars parked illegally will be towed away so use public transport whenever possible. The
nearest tube station is Arsenal (Piccadilly Line) which is 3 minutes walk from the ground with Finsbury Park (Victoria &
Piccadilly Lines) and Highbury & Islington about 10 minutes walk away.

ASTON VILLA FC

Photo courtesy of Neville Williams/Aston Villa FC

Founded: 1874 (**Entered League**: 1888)
Former Names: None
Nicknames: 'The Villans' 'Villa'
Ground: Villa Park, Trinity Road, Birmingham B6 6HE
Ground Capacity: 42,785 (All seats)
Record Attendance: 76,588 (2nd March 1946)
Pitch Size: 115 × 75 yards

Colours: Claret shirts with Blue sleeves, White shorts
Telephone Nº: (0121) 327-2299
Fax Number: (0121) 322-2107
Consumer Sales: 0330 053-6010
Web Site: www.avfc.co.uk

GENERAL INFORMATION

Ground Tours: 0800 612-0970
Car Parking: Please check the web site for information.
Away Coach Parking: Opposite the ground on Witton Lane
Nearest Railway Station: Witton or Aston (5 mins. walk)
Nearest Bus Station: Birmingham Centre
Club Shop: 'Villa Village' at the ground + also at New Street in Birmingham City Centre
Opening Times: Villa Village: Monday to Saturday 9.00am to 5.00pm and Sundays 11.00am to 4.00pm.
City Centre Store: Monday to Saturday 9.30am to 6.00pm and Sundays 11.00am to 3.00pm.
Telephone Nº: 08000 149346 Online store – Lines open Monday to Saturday 9.00am to 5.00pm (6.00pm weekdays)

GROUND INFORMATION

Away Supporters' Entrances & Sections:
Doug Ellis Stand – Blocks 'P' & 'Q'

ADMISSION INFO (2017/2018 PRICES)

Adult Seating: £20.00 – £37.00
Under-18s Seating: £13.00 – £37.00
Under-8s Seating: £10.00 – £37.00
Concessionary Seating: £15.00 – £30.00
Programme Price: £3.50
Note: Prices vary depending on the category of the game and the location in the stadium. Discounted 'Early Bird' prices apply for advance purchases in some areas of the stadium.

FANS WITH DISABILITIES INFORMATION

Wheelchairs: 84 spaces in total in the Trinity Road Stand lower, 8 of which are for away supporters
Helpers: Admitted on request – one per fan with disabilities
Prices: £15.00 – £28.00 for fans with disabilities
Disabled Toilets: Available in the Trinity Road Stand lower
Contact: 0800 612-0970 ext. 344 (Bookings are necessary)
E-mail contact: disability@avfc.co.uk

Travelling Supporters' Information: From all parts: Exit M6 at Junction 6 (Spaghetti Junction). Follow signs for Birmingham (NE). Take the 4th exit at the roundabout onto the A38 (M) signposted Aston. After ½ mile, turn right into Aston Hall Road.
Bus Services: Service 7 from Colmore Circus to Witton Square. Also some specials.

BARNET FC

Founded: 1888
Former Names: Barnet Alston FC
Nickname: 'The Bees'
Ground: The Hive, Camrose Avenue, Edgware, HA8 6AG
Record Attendance: 5,176
Pitch Size: 112 × 73 yards

Colours: Shirts and shorts are Black and Amber
Telephone Nº: (020) 8381-3800
Ticket Office: (020) 8381-3800
Ground Capacity: 5,233
Seating Capacity: 3,434
Web site: www.barnetfc.com
E-mail: tellus@barnetfc.com

GENERAL INFORMATION

Car Parking: 350 spaces available at the ground
Coach Parking: Available at the ground
Nearest Railway Station: Harrow & Wealdstone (2½ miles)
Nearest Tube Station: Canons Park (5 minutes walk)
Club Shop: At the ground
Opening Times: Daily from 6.00am to midnight – the shop is open throughout The Hive opening hours.
Telephone Nº: (020) 8381-3800

GROUND INFORMATION

Away Supporters' Entrances & Sections:
North Terrace and North West corner

ADMISSION INFO (2017/2018 PRICES)

Adult Standing: £19.00
Adult Seating: £19.00 – £25.00
Concessionary Seating: £10.00 – £14.00
Junior Bees (Under-14s): £5.00
Away Supporter Seating: £23.00
Programme Price: £3.00

FANS WITH DISABILITIES INFORMATION

Wheelchairs: 43 covered spaces in total for Home and Away fans in the East and West Stands
Helpers: One helper admitted per wheelchair
Prices: Normal prices for fans with disabilities. Helpers free
Disabled Toilets: Available
Contact: (020) 8381-3800 (Bookings are advisable)

Travelling Supporters' Information:
Routes: Exit the M1 at Junction 4 and take the Edgware Way/Watford Bypass (A41). Take the 3rd exit at the roundabout onto the A410 then the first exit at the next roundabout along the A5 (Stonegrove), continuing for approximately 1½ miles. Turn right into Camrose Avenue and The Hive is approximately two-thirds of a mile along this road.

BARNSLEY FC

Founded: 1887 (**Entered League**: 1898)
Former Names: Barnsley St. Peter's
Nickname: 'Reds'
Ground: Oakwell Stadium, Barnsley   S71 1ET
Ground Capacity: 23,176 (All seats)
Record Attendance: 40,255 (15th February 1936)
Pitch Size: 110 × 72 yards

Colours: Red shirts with White shorts and Red socks
Telephone N°: (01226) 211211
Ticket Office: (01226) 211183
Fax Number: (01226) 211444
Web Site: www.barnsleyfc.co.uk
E-mail: thereds@barnsleyfc.co.uk

GENERAL INFORMATION
Car Parking: Queen's Ground Car Park (adjacent)
Coach Parking: Queen's Ground Car Park
Nearest Railway Station: Barnsley Interchange (6 minutes walk)
Nearest Bus Station: Barnsley Interchange
Club Shop: At the Stadium
Opening Times: Monday to Friday 9.00am to 5.00pm. Saturdays 9.00am to 2.00pm. Saturday Matchdays open 9.00am to 3.00pm then 4.45pm to 5.15pm. Evening matchdays open 9.00am to 7.45pm
Telephone N°: (01226) 211400

GROUND INFORMATION
Away Supporters' Entrances & Sections:
North Stand Turnstiles 42-51

ADMISSION INFO (2017/2018 PRICES)
Adult Seating: £25.00 – £38.00
Ages 17-21 Seating: £18.00 – £26.00
Ages 12-16 Seating: £12.00
Under-12s Seating: £7.00
Concessionary Seating: £18.00 – £26.00
Note: Prices are lower for tickets purchased in advance and prices vary depending on the category of the game.
Programme Price: £3.00

FANS WITH DISABILITIES INFORMATION
Wheelchairs: A special stand provides accommodation for those in wheelchairs and blind supporters.
Helpers: Admitted depending on room available
Prices: £25.00 for fans with disabilities but helpers are admitted free of charge
Disabled Toilets: Available in the Corner Stand, North Stand and C.K. Beckett Stand
Commentaries are available for the blind
Contact: 0871 226-6777 (Bookings are necessary)

Travelling Supporters' Information: From All Parts: Exit the M1 at Junction 37 and follow the 'Barnsley FC/Football Ground' signs which lead to a large surface car park adjacent to the stadium (2 miles).

BIRMINGHAM CITY FC

Founded: 1875 (**Entered League**: 1892)
Former Names: Small Heath Alliance FC (1875-88); Small Heath FC (1888-1905); Birmingham FC (1905-45)
Nickname: 'The Blues'
Ground: St. Andrew's Stadium, Birmingham B9 4RL
Ground Capacity: 29,409 (All seats)
Record Attendance: 68,844 (11th February 1939)

Pitch Size: 109 × 74 yards
Colours: Royal Blue Shirts with White Shorts
Telephone Nº: (0121) 772-0101
Ticket Office: (0121) 772-0101 (Option 2)
Fax Number: (0121) 766-7866
Web Site: www.bcfc.com
E-mail: reception@bcfc.com

GENERAL INFORMATION

Car Parking: Street Parking + Birmingham Wheels (secure parking but not related to the club)
Coach Parking: Coventry Road
Nearest Railway Station: Birmingham New Street or Birmingham Moor Street (20 minutes walk)
Nearest Bus Station: Digbeth National Express Coach Station
Club Shops: Blues Store at the ground
Opening Times: Monday to Saturday 9.00am to 5.00pm
Telephone Nº: (0121) 772-0101 (Option 4)

GROUND INFORMATION

Away Supporters' Entrances & Sections:
Gil Merrick Stand, Coventry Road

ADMISSION INFO (2017/2018 PRICES)

Adult Seating: £15.00 – £35.00
Under-19s Seating: £10.00 – £25.00
Under-13s Seating: £5.00 – £20.00
Concessionary Seating: £10.00 – £30.00
Note: Prices vary depending on the category of the match and the location of the seat.

FANS WITH DISABILITIES INFORMATION

Wheelchairs: Spaces available in the Spion Kop Stand, Gil Merrick Lower Stand, Tilton Road Stand and West Paddocks
Helpers: One assistant admitted for each fan with disabilities
Prices: Normal prices apply for fans with disabilities and their helpers
Disabled Toilets: Available in the Spion Kop Stand, Family Stand, Gil Merrick Stand and Tilton Road Stand
Contact: (0121) 772-0101 Option 2 (Bookings are necessary)

Travelling Supporters' Information: From All Parts: Exit M6 at Junction 6 and take the A38 (M) (Aston Expressway). Leave at 2nd exit then take first exit at roundabout along the Dartmouth Middleway. After 1¼ miles turn left on to Coventry Road.
Bus Services: Services 17, 58, 59 & 60 from Birmingham Centre stop at Cattell Road just to the south of the stadium and Services 97f stops at Garrison Lane just to the north of the stadium.

BLACKBURN ROVERS FC

Founded: 1875 (**Entered League**: 1888)
Nickname: 'Rovers' 'Blues & Whites'
Ground: Ewood Park, Blackburn,
Lancashire   BB2 4JF
Pitch Size: 115 × 72 yards
Ground Capacity: 31,367 (All seats)
Record Attendance: 62,255 vs Bolton (2/3/1929)

Colours: Blue and White halved shirts, White shorts
Telephone Nº: (01254) 372001
Ticket Office: (01254) 372000
Fax Number: (01254) 671042
Web Site: www.rovers.co.uk

GENERAL INFORMATION

Car Parking: 800 spaces available at the ground
Coach Parking: At the ground (Darwen End)
Nearest Railway Station: Blackburn Central (1½ miles)
Nearest Bus Station: Blackburn Central (1½ miles)
Club Shop: Roverstore at the ground
Opening Times: Weekdays 9.00am – 5.30pm, Saturday
10.00am–4.00pm, closed on Sundays.
Telephone Nº: (01254) 508137 (Ewood shop)

GROUND INFORMATION

Away Supporters' Entrances & Sections:
Darwen End

ADMISSION INFO (2017/2018 PRICES)

Adult Seating: £25.00 – £31.00
Child Seating: £4.00 – £11.00 (Age dependent)
Concessions Seating: £11.00 – £26.00
Student Seating: £11.00 – £26.00
Programme Price: £3.00

FANS WITH DISABILITIES INFORMATION

Wheelchairs: 262 spaces for Home fans and 30 for Away fans
Helpers: One helper admitted per fan with disabilities.
Applications for helpers tickets must be made in advance
Prices: Normal prices apply for both fans with disabilities
and their helpers
Disabled Toilets: 14 purpose-built ground level toilets
Commentaries available via Radio Rovers – bring a radio!
Contact: 0771 772-4646   **E-mail**: disability@rovers.co.uk

Travelling Supporters' Information: Routes: Supporters travelling Northbound on the M6: Exit the M6 at Junction 29, follow the M65 and exit at Junction 4 for Ewood Park. The ground is ¾ mile from Junction 4 – please look for parking areas to avoid congestion around the ground; Supporters travelling Northbound on the M61: Exit the M61 at Junction 9, join the M65 and exit at Junction 4 (then as above); Supporters travelling Southbound on the M6: Exit the M6 at Junction 30, follow the M61 and exit at Junction 9 onto the M65. Exit the M65 at Junction 4 for the ground; Supporters from the Yorkshire Area either on the B6234, the A56 Haslingden by-pass or the A59 Skipton Road – please follow signs for Ewood Park (follow Preston M65 and exit at Junction 4).

BLACKPOOL FC

Founded: 1887 (**Entered League**: 1896)
Former Name: Merged with Blackpool St. Johns (1887)
Nickname: 'Seasiders' or 'Tangerines'
Ground: Bloomfield Road, Blackpool, FY1 6JJ
Ground Capacity: 16,750 (All seats)
Record Attendance: 38,098 (17th September 1955)
Pitch Size: 110 × 74 yards

Colours: Tangerine shirts with White shorts
Telephone Nº: (01253) 685000
Ticket Office: 0844 847-1953
Fax Number: (01253) 405011
Web Site: www.blackpoolfc.co.uk
E-mail: ticketoffice@blackpoolfc.co.uk

GENERAL INFORMATION

Car Parking: 3,000 spaces at the ground and street parking
Coach Parking: Available at the ground
Nearest Railway Station: Blackpool South (5 mins. walk)
Nearest Bus Station: Talbot Road (2 miles)
Club Shop: At the ground
Opening Times: Daily from 9.00am to 5.15pm
Telephone Nº: (01253) 685025

GROUND INFORMATION

Away Supporters' Entrances & Sections:
Blocks A and B in the North Stand

ADMISSION INFO (2017/2018 PRICES)

Adult Seating: £22.00 – £27.00
Under-19s Seating: £10.00 – £15.00
Senior Citizen Seating: £18.00 – £23.00
Note: 'Young Seasider' members (Under-11s) are admitted free of charge.
Programme Price: £3.00

FANS WITH DISABILITIES INFORMATION

Wheelchairs: Over 50 spaces in total for home and away fans
Helpers: One helper admitted with each fan with disabilities
Prices: Normal prices apply
Disabled Toilets: Available
Contact: 07875 236576 (Bookings are necessary)

Travelling Supporters' Information: From All Parts: Exit M6 at Junction 32 onto the M55. Follow signs for the main car parks along the new 'spine' road to the car parks at the side of the ground.

BOLTON WANDERERS FC

Founded: 1874 (**Entered League**: 1888)
Former Names: Christchurch FC (1874-1877)
Nickname: 'Trotters'
Ground: Macron Stadium, Burnden Way, Lostock, Bolton, Lancashire   BL6 6JW
Ground Capacity: 28,723 (All seats)
Pitch Size: 110 × 70 yards

Record Attendance: 27,409
Colours: White shirts with Navy Blue shorts
Telephone Nº: (01204) 673673
Ticket Office: 0844 871-2932
Fax Number: (01204) 673773
Web Site: www.bwfc.co.uk
E-mail: reception@bwfc.co.uk

GENERAL INFORMATION
Car Parking: 2,800 spaces available at the ground
Coach Parking: Available at the ground
Nearest Railway Station: Horwich Parkway (600 yards)
Nearest Bus Station: Moor Lane, Bolton
Club Shop: At the ground
Opening Times: Daily from 9.30am to 5.30pm
Telephone Nº: (01204) 673650

GROUND INFORMATION
Away Supporters' Entrances & Sections:
South Stand entrances and accommodation

ADMISSION INFO (2017/2018 PRICES)
Adult Seating: £15.00 – £35.00
Concessionary Seating: £7.00 – £29.00
Under-18s Seating: £7.00 – £12.00
Under-12s Seating: £7.00 – £10.00
Note: Prices vary depending on the grading of the game

FANS WITH DISABILITIES INFORMATION
Wheelchairs: 32 spaces available for visiting fans, 72 spaces for home fans
Helpers: One helper admitted with each fan with disabilities
Prices: Please contact the club for details
Disabled Toilets: Available
Contact: 0844 871-2932 (Bookings are necessary)

Travelling Supporters' Information:
From All Parts: Exit the M61 at Junction 6 and the ground is clearly visible ¼ mile away.

BRADFORD CITY FC

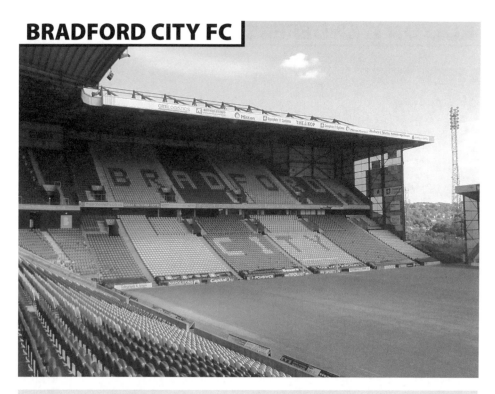

Founded: 1903 (**Entered League**: 1903)
Nickname: 'Bantams'
Ground: Valley Parade, Bradford   BD8 7DY
Ground Capacity: 25,136 (All seats)
Record Attendance: 39,146 (11th March 1911)
Pitch Size: 113 × 70 yards

Colours: Claret and Amber diagonally striped shirts with Black shorts
Telephone Nº: 0871 978-1911
Ticket Office: 0871-978-8000
Fax Number: (01274) 773356
Web Site: www.bradfordcityfc.co.uk
E-mail: bradfordcityfc@compuserve.com

GENERAL INFORMATION

Car Parking: Street Parking and Car Parks (£3.00 charge)
Coach Parking: By Police direction
Nearest Railway Station: Bradford Foster Square
Nearest Bus Station: Bradford Interchange (1 mile)
Club Shop: At the ground
Opening Times: Monday to Saturday 10.00am to 3.00pm
Telephone Nº: (01274) 309945
Shop Web Site: www.thecityshop.co.uk

GROUND INFORMATION

Away Supporters' Entrances & Sections:
Midland Road Stand entrances and accommodation

ADMISSION INFO (2017/2018 PRICES)

Adult Seating: £25.00 (£20.00 purchased in advance)
Under-16s Seating: £10.00
Senior Citizen Seating: £15.00
Note: Under-11s are admitted for £5.00 when accompanied by a paying adult – up to 3 Under-11s admitted per adult.
Programme Price: £3.00

FANS WITH DISABILITIES INFORMATION

Wheelchairs: 100 spaces available in total for Home and Away fans in special areas in 'A' Block of the JCT600 Stand and the Kop Stand and Northern Commercials Stand
Helpers: One helper admitted per fan with disabilities
Prices: Normal prices for fans with disabilities. Helpers free
Disabled Toilets: Available
Contact: 0871 978-8000   (Bookings are necessary)

Travelling Supporters' Information: Routes: Exit the M62 at Junction 26 and take the M606 towards Bradford. At the end of the motorway get in the middle lane and follow signs for Bradford (West) into Rooley Lane (signs for the Airport). A McDonalds is now on your left. Turn left into Wakefield Road at the roundabout and stay in the middle lane. Continue straight on over two roundabouts (signs to Shipley and Skipton) onto Shipley Airedale Road which then becomes Canal Road. Just after Tesco on the left, turn left into Station Road and left again into Queens Road. Go up the hill to the third set of traffic lights and turn left into Manningham Lane. After the Gulf petrol station on the left, turn first left into Valley Parade for the Stadium.

BRENTFORD FC

Photo courtesy of Mark Chapman

Founded: 1889 (**Entered League**: 1920)
Nickname: 'The Bees'
Ground: Griffin Park, Braemar Road, Brentford, Middlesex TW8 0NT
Ground Capacity: 12,573
Seating Capacity: 8,949
Record Attendance: 38,678 (26th February 1949)

Pitch Size: 110 × 74 yards
Colours: Red & White striped shirts with Black shorts
Telephone Nº: 0845 3456-442
Ticket Office: 0845 3456-442
Fax Number: (020) 8568-9940
Web Site: www.brentfordfc.co.uk
E-mail: enquiries@brentfordfc.co.uk

GENERAL INFORMATION

Car Parking: Street Parking
Coach Parking: By Police direction
Nearest Railway Station: Brentford (½ mile)
Nearest Tube Station: South Ealing (Piccadilly) (1 mile)
Club Shop: Adjacent to the ground in Braemar Road
Opening Times: Weekdays 10.00am–4.00pm and Matchdays 12.00pm – 6.00pm
Telephone Nº: 0845 3456-442

GROUND INFORMATION

Away Supporters' Entrances & Sections:
Brook Road Upper and Lower for both seating and terracing

ADMISSION INFO (2017/2018 PRICES)

Adult Standing: £23.00 – £25.00
Adult Seating: £23.00 – £30.00
Under-18s Standing/Seating: £6.00 – £8.00
Senior Citizen Standing: £17.00 – £19.00
Senior Citizen Seating: £17.00 – £24.00
Ages 18 to 24 Standing: £15.00 – £17.00
Ages 18 to 24 Seating: £15.00 – £22.00
Programme Price: £3.00

FANS WITH DISABILITIES INFORMATION

Wheelchairs: 10 spaces for Home fans, 2 spaces for Away fans in a special section in the Braemar Road Stand
Helpers: One helper admitted per fan with disabilities
Prices: Normal prices for fans with disabilities. Helpers free
Disabled Toilets: Available in the Braemar Road Stand
Commentaries are available for the blind
Contact: 0845 3456-442   (Bookings are necessary)

Travelling Supporters' Information: Routes: From the North: Take the A406 North Circular (from the M1/A1) to the Chiswick Roundabout and then along the Great West Road and turn left at the third set of traffic lights into Ealing Road for the ground; From the East: Take the A406 to the Chiswick Roundabout, then as North; From the West: Exit M4 at Junction 2 – down to the Chiswick Roundabout, then as North; From the South: Use the A3, M3, A240 or A316 to Kew Road, continue along over Kew Bridge, turn left at the traffic lights, then right at the next traffic lights into Ealing Road.

BRIGHTON & HOVE ALBION FC

Founded: 1901 (**Entered League**: 1920)
Nickname: 'Seagulls'
Ground: American Express Community Stadium, Village Way, Brighton BN1 9BL
Ground Capacity: 30,303 (All seats)
Pitch Size: 115 × 75 yards
Record Attendance: 30,003 (at Amex Stadium)

Colours: Blue & White striped shirts with Blue shorts
Telephone Nº: 0344 324-6282
Ticket Office: 0844 327-1901
Fax Number: (01273) 878238
Web Site: www.seagulls.co.uk
E-mail: supporter.services@bhafc.co.uk

GENERAL INFORMATION

Car Parking: Limited parking at the stadium and 700 spaces available at the University campus (adjacent)
Coach Parking: At the stadium
Nearest Railway Station: Falmer (adjacent)
Nearest Bus Station: Brighton
Club Shop: At the stadium
Opening Times: Monday to Saturday 9.30am to 5.00pm and Sundays 11.00am to 4.00pm
Telephone Nº: 0845 496-9442

GROUND INFORMATION

Away Supporters' Entrances & Sections: South Stand

ADMISSION INFO (2017/2018 PRICES)

Adult Seating: £30.00 – £60.00
Under-18s Seating: £15.00 – £30.00
Under-21s/Senior Citizen Seating: £23.00 – £42.00
Note: Prices vary depending on the category of the game
Programme Price: £3.50

FANS WITH DISABILITIES INFORMATION

Wheelchairs: Approximately 250 spaces available in total
Helpers: One helper admitted per fan with disabilities
Prices: Normal prices for fans with disabilities. Helpers free
Disabled Toilets: Yes – in all the stands
Contact: 0844 327-1901   (Bookings are necessary)

Travelling Supporters' Information: Routes: From the North: Take the M23 then the A23 to Brighton. At the roundabout on the outskirts of Brighton, take the exit onto the A27 towards Lewes. Pass the A270 turn-off and continue towards the village of Falmer. The stadium is situated by the side of the A27 in the village of Falmer across the road from the University of Sussex campus; From the East and West: Take the A27 to Falmer which is located to the north-east of Brighton. Then as above.

BRISTOL CITY FC

Founded: 1894 (**Entered League**: 1901)
Former Name: Bristol South End FC (1894-1897)
Nickname: 'The Robins'
Ground: Ashton Gate Stadium, Bristol   BS3 2EJ
Ground Capacity: 21,497 (All seats)
Pitch Size: 115 × 75 yards
Record Attendance: 43,335 (16th February 1935)

Colours: Red shirts with White shorts
Telephone Nº: (0117) 963-0600
Ticket Hotline: (0117) 963-0600 (Option 1)
Fax Number: (0117) 963-0700
Web Site: www.bcfc.co.uk
E-mail: enquiries@bcfc.co.uk

GENERAL INFORMATION

Car Parking: Street parking
Coach Parking: By prior arrangement with the club
Nearest Railway Station: Bristol Temple Meads (1½ miles)
Nearest Bus Station: Bristol City Centre
Club Shop: BCFC Megastore at the ground
Opening Times: Monday 10.00am to 5.00pm, Tuesday to Friday 9.00am to 5.00pm and Saturdays 9.00am to 1.00pm (open until kick-off on Matchdays)
Telephone Nº: (0117) 963-0600 (Option 0 then Option 1)

GROUND INFORMATION

Away Supporters' Entrances & Sections:
Wedlock Stand
Note: During the ongoing ground redevelopment , restrictions may apply for away fans.

ADMISSION INFO (2017/2018 PRICES)

Adult Seating: £21.00 – £41.00
Under-25s/Senior Citizen Seating: £19.00 – £38.00
Under-19s Seating: £11.00 – £23.00
Under-12s Seating: £5.00 – £17.00
Note: A membership scheme offers discounted prices for advance bookings. Prices vary depending on game category
Programme Price: £3.00

FANS WITH DISABILITIES INFORMATION

Wheelchairs: Limited number accommodated at pitchside – please apply early
Helpers: One helper admitted per fan with disabilities
Prices: Normal prices for fans with disabilities. Helpers free
Disabled Toilets: Available in various areas of the ground
Commentaries are available for the blind
Contact: (0117) 963-0600 Option 1 (Bookings are necessary)

Travelling Supporters' Information: Routes: From the North & West: Exit the M5 at Junction 16, take the A38 to Bristol City Centre and follow the A38 Taunton signs. Cross the swing bridge after 1¼ miles and bear left into Winterstoke Road for the ground; From the East: Take the M4 then M32 and follow signs for the City Centre. Then as for North and West; From the South: Exit the M5 at Junction 19 and follow Taunton signs over the swing bridge (then as above).
Away Fans Car Parking: Bedminster Cricket Club, Clanidge Road, Bristol – SatNav: BS3 2JX (½ mile from Ashton Gate)
Bus Services: Services 27A and 28A from Bristol Temple Meads Station. A bus leaves Temple Meads 1 hour prior to kick-off.

BRISTOL ROVERS FC

Founded: 1883   (**Re-entered League**: 2015)
Former Names: Black Arabs FC (1883-84);
Eastville Rovers FC (1884-96);
Bristol Eastville Rovers FC (1896-97)
Nickname: 'Pirates' 'Rovers' 'Gas'
Ground: Memorial Stadium, Filton Avenue, Horfield,
Bristol   BS7 0BF
Pitch Size: 110 × 71 yards

Ground Capacity: 11,917
Seating Capacity: 3,307
Record Attendance: 12,011 (9th March 2008)
Colours: Blue & White quartered shirts, White shorts
Telephone Nº: (0117) 909-6648
Fax Number: (0117) 907-4312
Web Site: www.bristolrovers.co.uk

GENERAL INFORMATION

Car Parking: Very limited number of spaces at the ground and street parking
Coach Parking: At the ground
Nearest Railway Station: Temple Meads (2 miles)
Nearest Bus Station: Bristol City Centre
Club Shop: 199 Two Mile Hill Road, Kingswood and also at Pirate Leisure, Memorial Stadium, Filton Avenue
Opening Times: Supporters' Club: Weekdays 9.00am to 5.00pm and Saturdays 9.00am to 1.00pm; Pirate Leisure: Weekdays 9.00am to 5.00pm, Saturdays 9.00am to 1.00pm (Home matchdays 9.00am – 3.00pm then 4.45pm – 5.15pm)
Telephone Nº: (0117) 961-1772 + (0117) 909-6648

GROUND INFORMATION

Away Supporters' Entrances & Sections:
Entrance to East Terrace & South Stand via Filton Avenue

ADMISSION INFO (2017/2018 PRICES)

Adult Standing: £18.00 – £20.00
Adult Seating: £20.50 – £26.00
Concessionary Standing: £7.00 – £11.00
Concessionary Seating: £11.50 – £20.50
Note: A discount of £2.00 per ticket is available if purchased prior to the matchday.
Programme Price: £3.00

FANS WITH DISABILITIES INFORMATION

Wheelchairs: Unspecified number accommodated in front of the East Stand and West Stand
Helpers: One helper admitted per fan with disabilities
Prices: £11.50 for both fans in wheelchairs and the ambulant. Helpers are admitted free of charge
Disabled Toilets: Available in the East Stand and West Stand
Contact: (0117) 909-6648 Option 1 (Bookings are necessary)

Travelling Supporters' Information: Routes: From All Parts: Exit the M32 at Junction 2 then take the exit at the roundabout (signposted Horfield) into Muller Road. Continue for approximately 1½ miles passing straight across 3 sets of traffic lights. At the 6th set of traffic lights turn left into Filton Avenue and the ground is immediately on the left.

BURNLEY FC

Founded: 1882 (**Entered League**: 1888)
Former Name: Burnley Rovers FC
Nickname: 'Clarets'
Ground: Turf Moor, Harry Potts Way, Burnley, Lancashire BB10 4BX
Ground Capacity: 21,401 (All seats)
Record Attendance: 54,775 (23rd February 1924)

Pitch Size: 113 × 71 yards
Colours: Claret and Sky Blue shirts and shorts
Telephone Nº: (01282) 446800
Ticket Office: 0844 807-1882
Fax Number: (01282) 700014
Web Site: www.burnleyfootballclub.com
E-mail: info@burnleyfc.com

GENERAL INFORMATION

Car Parking: Matchday parking restrictions in surrounding streets so it is recommended that the various Town Centre car parks are used by visiting fans.
Coach Parking: By Police direction
Nearest Railway Station: Burnley Central (1½ miles)
Nearest Bus Station: Burnley (5 minutes walk)
Club Shop: At the ground
Opening Times: Monday to Saturday 9.00am – 5.30pm; Sundays 10.00am – 4.00pm
Telephone Nº: (01282) 700016

GROUND INFORMATION

Away Supporters' Entrances & Sections:
David Fishwick Stand

ADMISSION INFO (2017/2018 PRICES)

Adult Seating: £30.00 – £40.00
Under-18s Seating: £15.00 – £20.00
Under-12s Seating: £10.00 (with a paying adult in the Family Stand only)
Under-22s/Senior Citizen Seating: £20.00 – £25.00
Programme Price: £3.00

FANS WITH DISABILITIES INFORMATION

Wheelchairs: Four designated wheelchair areas
Helpers: One helper admitted for each wheelchair user
Prices: Normal prices apply for fans with disabilities plus one helper admitted free of charge
Disabled Toilets: Available
Commentary radios are available to purchase for a nominal fee.
Contact: (01282) 446800 (Bookings are necessary)

Travelling Supporters' Information: Routes: From the North: Follow the A682 to the Town Centre and take first exit at roundabout (Gala Club) into Yorkshire Street. Follow through traffic signals into Harry Potts Way; From the East: Follow the A646 to the A671 then along Todmorden Road towards the Town Centre. At the traffic signals (crossroads) turn right into Harry Potts Way; From the West & South: Exit the M6 at Junction 29 onto the M65. Exit the M65 at Junction 10 and follow signs for Burnley Football Club. At the roundabout in the town centre take the third exit into Yorkshire Street. Then as from the North.

BURTON ALBION FC

Founded: 1950 **(Entered League**: 2009)
Former Names: None
Nickname: 'The Brewers'
Ground: The Pirelli Stadium, Princess Way,
Burton-on-Trent   DE13 0AR
Record Attendance: 6,192 (17th April 2009)
Pitch Size: 110 × 72 yards

Colours: Yellow shirts with Black trim, Black shorts
Telephone Nº: (01283) 565938
Fax Number: (01283) 523199
Ground Capacity: 6,912 **Seating Capacity**: 2,000
Web site: www.burtonalbionfc.co.uk
E-mail: bafc@burtonalbionfc.co.uk

GENERAL INFORMATION
Supporters Club: c/o Club
Telephone Nº: (01283) 565938
Car Parking: 400 spaces available at the ground
Coach Parking: Rykneld Trading Estate, Derby Road
Nearest Railway Station: Burton-on-Trent (1½ miles)
Nearest Bus Station: Burton-on-Trent (1½ miles)
Club Shop: At the ground
Opening Times: Weekdays 8.30am to 5.30pm and
Matchdays from 9.00am until kick-off
Telephone Nº: (01283) 565938

GROUND INFORMATION
Away Supporters' Entrances & Sections:
East Stand, Derby Road

ADMISSION INFO (2017/2018 PRICES)
Adult Standing: £20.00   **Adult Seating**: £24.00
Under-17s Standing: £7.00 **Under-17s Seating**: £14.00
Ages 17 to 22 Standing: £15.00   **Seating**: £22.00
Senior Citizen Standing: £18.00   **Seating**: £22.00
Programme Price: £3.00

FANS WITH DISABILITIES INFORMATION
Wheelchairs: Over 78 spaces available for home and away
fans in designated areas
Helpers: Admitted
Prices: Normal prices for fans with disabilities. Helpers free
Disabled Toilets: Available in all stands
Contact: (01283) 565938   (Bookings are necessary)

Travelling Supporters' Information:
Routes: From the M1, North and South: Exit at Junction 23A and join the A50 towards Derby (also signposted for Alton
Towers). Join the A38 southbound at the Toyota factory (towards Burton & Lichfield) then exit for Burton North onto the A5121.
Continue past the Pirelli factory on the right and the BP Garage and Cash & Carry on the left then turn into Princess Way at the
roundabout; From the M5/6 South: Join the M42 northbound and exit onto the A446 signposted Lichfield. Follow signs for
the A38 to Burton then exit onto A5121 as above; From the M6 North: Exit at Junction 15 and follow the A50 towards Stoke
and Uttoxeter. Exit the A50 for the A38 southbound signposted Burton and Lichfield at the Toyota factory, then as above.
SatNav users should enter the following post code: DE13 0BH

BURY FC

Founded: 1885 (**Entered League**: 1894)
Nickname: 'Shakers'
Ground: Gigg Lane, Bury, Lancashire BL9 9HR
Ground Capacity: 11,313 (All seats)
Pitch Size: 112 × 73 yards
Record Attendance: 35,000 (9th January 1960)

Colours: White shirts with Royal Blue shorts & socks
Telephone Nº: (0161) 764-4881
Ticket Office: (0161) 764-4881 Option 1
General Fax Number: (0161) 764-5521
Web Site: www.buryfc.co.uk
E-mail: admin@buryfc.co.uk

GENERAL INFORMATION
Car Parking: Designated car parks only
Coach Parking: By Police direction
Nearest Railway Station: Bury Interchange (1 mile)
Nearest Bus Station: Bury Interchange
Club Shop: At the ground
Opening Times: Monday to Friday and Saturday matchdays 10.00am to 5.00pm.
Telephone Nº: (0161) 764-4881 Option 1

GROUND INFORMATION
Away Supporters' Entrances & Sections:
Gigg Lane entrance for the East Stand

ADMISSION INFO (2017/2018 PRICES)
Adult Seating: £20.00
Concessionary Seating: £14.00
Under-18s Seating: £10.00
Under-12s Seating: £5.00
Under-5s Seating: Free of charge
Programme Price: £3.00

FANS WITH DISABILITIES INFORMATION
Wheelchairs: Spaces for 26 wheelchairs in home fans area and a further 25 spaces in the Away Supporters' Section
Helpers: One helper admitted per wheelchair
Prices: £14.00 for fans with disabilities. Free for helpers
Disabled Toilets: Available
A Radio Commentary is available in the Press Box for the Registered Blind
Contact: (0161) 764-4881 (Bookings are not necessary)

Travelling Supporters' Information: Routes: From the North: Exit the M66 at Junction 2, take Bury Road (A58) for ½ mile, then turn left into Heywood Street and follow this into Parkhills Road until its end, turn left into Manchester Road (A56) and then left again into Gigg Lane. From the South, East and West: Exit the M60 at Junction 17, take Bury Road (A56) for 3 miles and then turn right into Gigg Lane.

CAMBRIDGE UNITED FC

Founded: 1912 (**Re-entered League**: 2014)
Former Name: Abbey United FC (1912-1951)
Nickname: 'U's' 'United'
Ground: Abbey Stadium, Newmarket Road, Cambridge CB5 8LN
Ground Capacity: 8,339
Seating Capacity: 4,376
Pitch Size: 110 × 74 yards

Record Attendance: 14,000 (1st May 1970)
Colours: Amber and Black striped shirts, Black shorts
Telephone Nº: (01223) 566500
Ticket Office: (01223) 566500 (Option 1)
Fax Number: (01223) 729220
Web Site: www.cambridge-united.co.uk
E-mail: info@cambridge-united.co.uk

GENERAL INFORMATION
Car Parking: Street parking only
Coach Parking: Coldhams Road
Nearest Railway Station: Cambridge (2 miles)
Nearest Bus Station: Cambridge City Centre
Club Shop: At the ground
Opening Times: Monday to Friday 9.30am to 4.00pm and Matchdays 11.00am to kick-off
Telephone Nº: (01223) 566500

GROUND INFORMATION
Away Supporters' Entrances & Sections:
Coldham Common turnstiles 20-22 – Habbin Terrace (South) and South Stand (Seating) turnstiles 23-26

ADMISSION INFO (2017/2018 PRICES)
Adult Standing: £16.00
Adult Seating: £18.00 – £22.00
Junior Standing: £8.00
Junior Seating: £8.00 – £10.00
Concessionary Standing: £12.00
Concessionary Seating: £13.00 – £22.00

FANS WITH DISABILITIES INFORMATION
Wheelchairs: 19 spaces in total for Home fans in sections in front of Main Stand and in the North Terrace. 16 spaces for Away fans in the South Stand.
Helpers: One helper admitted per fan with disabilities
Prices: £12.00 – £15.00 for the disabled. Free for helpers
Disabled Toilets: Available
Contact: (01223) 566500 (Early booking strongly advised)

Travelling Supporters' Information: From the North: Take the A14 from Huntingdon, then turn east along the A14 dual carriageway. Exit the A14 at the 4th junction (to the east of Cambridge), up the slip road signposted Stow-cum-Quy then turn right onto the A1303, returning westwards towards Cambridge. Go straight on at the first roundabout passing the Airport on the left then straight on at two sets of traffic lights. Go straight on at the next roundabout and the ground is on the left after 700 yards; From the South: Exit the M11 at Junction 14 and turn east along the A14 dual carriageway. Then as from the North.
Bus Services: Services from the Railway Station to the City Centre and Nº 3 from the City Centre to the Ground.

CARDIFF CITY FC

Founded: 1899 (**Entered League**: 1920)
Former Names: Riverside FC (1899-1902) and
Riverside Albion FC (1902-1908)
Nickname: 'Bluebirds'
Ground: Cardiff City Stadium, Leckwith Road,
Cardiff CF11 8AZ
Record Attendance: 28,016 (24th November 2013)
Ground Capacity: 33,500 (All seats)

Pitch Size: 110 × 75 yards
Colours: Blue shirts with White shorts
Telephone Nº: 0845 365-1115
Away Support Ticket Office: 0845 345-1400
Fax Number: 0845 365-1116
Web Site: www.cardiffcityfc.co.uk
E-mail: club@cardiffcityfc.co.uk

GENERAL INFORMATION

Car Parking: Stadium car park and Street Parking
Coach Parking: Stadium car park (adjacent)
Nearest Railway Station: Cardiff Central (1 mile) and
also Ninian Park Station (500 yards)
Nearest Bus Station: Cardiff Central
Club Shop: At the ground
Opening Times: Weekdays from 9.00am to 5.00pm and
Saturdays 9.00am to 4.00pm
Telephone Nº: 0845 345-1485
Postal Sales: Yes (Internet Sales also accepted)

GROUND INFORMATION

Away Supporters' Entrances & Sections:
Grange End, Gate 07 – sections 119 to 122

ADMISSION INFO (2017/2018 PRICES)

Adult Seating: £15.00 – £34.00
Concessionary Seating: £12.00 – £27.00
Ages 16 to 21 Seating: £10.00 – £24.00
Under-16s Seating: £5.00 – £22.00
Note: Prices vary depending on the classification of the game
and cheaper prices are available in the Family area.

FANS WITH DISABILITIES INFORMATION

Wheelchairs: Numerous spaces available for fans with
disabilities in various areas around the ground
Helpers: One helper admitted per fan with disabilities
Prices: Normal prices for fans with disabilities. Helpers
admitted free of charge
Disabled Toilets: Available
Contact: 0845 345-1400 (Away fans tickets are normally
sold in advance but may be available on the day)

Travelling Supporters' Information:
Routes: From All Parts: Exit M4 at Junction 33 and follow Penarth (A4232) signs. After 6 miles, take the B4267 to Cardiff City
Stadium.

CARLISLE UNITED FC

Founded: 1903 (**Entered League**: 1928)
Former Names: Formed with the amalgamation of
Shaddongate United FC and Carlisle Red Rose FC
Nickname: 'Cumbrians' 'Blues'
Ground: Brunton Park Stadium, Warwick Road,
Carlisle   CA1 1LL
Ground Capacity: 17,949
Seating Capacity: 7,594

Record Attendance: 27,500 (5th January 1957)
Pitch Size: 112 × 74 yards
Colours: Royal Blue shirts with White shorts
Telephone Nº: (01228) 526237
Ticket Office: 0844 371-1921
Fax Number: (01228) 554141
Web Site: www.carlisleunited.co.uk
E-mail: enquiries@carlisleunited.co.uk

GENERAL INFORMATION

Car Parking: Rear of Ground via St. Aidans Road
Coach Parking: St. Aidans Road Car Park
Nearest Railway Station: Carlisle Citadel (1 mile)
Nearest Bus Station: Lowther Street, Carlisle
Club Shop: At the ground and in the City Centre
Opening Times: Monday to Saturday 10.00am – 5.00pm
Telephone Nº: (01228) 554138

GROUND INFORMATION

Away Supporters' Entrances & Sections:
Turnstiles 14-16 for the Petteril End or CBS Stand Section 2

ADMISSION INFO (2017/2018 PRICES)

Adult Standing: £16.00 – £19.00 **Seating**: £19 – £22
Ages 18-22 Standing: £10.00–£13.00 **Seating**: £13–£16
Ages 11-17 Standing: £7.00   **Seating**: £10.00
Under-11s Standing: £4.00   **Under-11s Seating**: £7.00
Under-7s: Admitted free of charge
Senior Citizen Standing: £13.00 – £16.00
Senior Citizen Seating: £16.00 – £19.00
Note: Tickets are cheaper if purchased before the matchday
Programme Price: £2.00

FANS WITH DISABILITIES INFORMATION

Wheelchairs: 23 spaces for wheelchairs in a special section.
Helpers: One helper admitted per fan with disabilities
Prices: Fans in wheelchairs are admitted for £4.00.
Helpers are admitted free of charge.
Disabled Toilets: Available
Contact: (01228) 526237   (Bookings are recommended)

Travelling Supporters' Information:
Routes: From the North, South and East: Exit the M6 at Junction 43 and follow signs for Carlisle (A69) into Warwick Road for
the ground; From the West: Take the A69 straight into Warwick Road.

CHARLTON ATHLETIC FC

Founded: 1905 (**Entered League**: 1921)
Nickname: 'Addicks'
Ground: The Valley, Floyd Road, Charlton, London, SE7 8BL
Ground Capacity: 27,111 (All seats)
Record Attendance: 75,031 (12th February 1938)
Pitch Size: 111 × 73 yards

Colours: Red shirts with White shorts
Telephone Nº: (020) 8333-4000
Ticket Office: 03330 144444
Fax Number: (020) 8333-4001
Web Site: www.cafc.co.uk
E-mail: customerservices@cafc.co.uk

GENERAL INFORMATION
Car Parking: Street Parking
Coach Parking: By Police direction
Nearest Railway Station: Charlton (2 minutes walk)
Nearest Bus Station: At Charlton Railway Station as above
Club Shop: At the ground
Opening Times: Weekdays 10.00am – 5.00pm
Non-Match Saturdays 10.00am – 4.00pm
Telephone Nº: (020) 8333-4035

GROUND INFORMATION
Away Supporters' Entrances & Sections:
Valley Grove/Jimmy Seed Stand

ADMISSION INFO (2016/2017 PRICES)
Adult Seating: £20.00 – £30.00
Under-18s Seating: £10.00
Under-11s Seating: £5.00
Concessionary Seating: £13.00 – £22.00
Programme Price: £3.00

FANS WITH DISABILITIES INFORMATION
Wheelchairs: 96 spaces available for Home fans in the West and East Stands. 7 spaces available for Away fans in the South (Jimmy Seed) Stand
Helpers: One helper admitted per fan with disabilities
Prices: Helpers are admitted free of charge. Fans in wheelchairs pay concessionary prices
Disabled Toilets: Available in West and East Stands
Commentaries are available – please ring for details
Contact: 03330 144444   (Bookings are necessary)

Travelling Supporters' Information:
Routes: From All Parts: Exit the M25 at Junction 2 (A2 London-bound) and follow until the road becomes the A102(M). Take the exit marked Woolwich Ferry and turn right along the A206 Woolwich Road. After approximately 1 mile do a U-turn at the roundabout back along Woolwich Road. At the traffic lights turn left into Charlton Church Lane and Floyd Road is the 2nd left.

CHELSEA FC

Founded: 1905 (**Entered League**: 1905)
Nickname: 'Blues'
Ground: Stamford Bridge, Fulham Road, London, SW6 1HS
Ground Capacity: 41,631 (All seats)
Record Attendance: 82,905 (12th October 1935)
Pitch Size: 113 × 74 yards

Colours: Blue shirts and shorts
Telephone Nº: 0371 811-1955
+44 207 386-9373 (International callers)
Ticket Office: 0371 811-1905
+44 207 835-6000 (International callers)
Fax Number: (020) 7381-4831
Web Site: www.chelseafc.com

GENERAL INFORMATION

Car Parking: Pre-booked underground car park at ground
Coach Parking: By Police direction
Nearest Tube Station: Fulham Broadway (District)
Club Shop: Chelsea Megastore – at the ground
Opening Times: Monday to Saturday 9.00am – 6.00pm; Sundays 11.00am–5.00pm; Bank Holidays 11.00am – 5.00pm Stadium tours are also available
Megastore Telephone Nº: 0371 811 1955

GROUND INFORMATION

Away Supporters' Entrances & Sections:
Shed End

ADMISSION INFO (2017/2018 PRICES)

Adult Seating: £47.00 – £87.00
Child Seating: £15.50 – £27.50
Senior Citizen Seating: £15.50 – £27.50
Note: Concessionary priced tickets are available in the Family Stand and East Upper Stand
Programme Price: £3.00

FANS WITH DISABILITIES INFORMATION

Seating: 258 spaces in total (including personal assistants) for Home and Away fans in the disabled area
Personal Assistants: One admitted per fan with disabilities
Prices: Free of charge for fans with disabilities
Disabled Toilets: Available in the East Stand Concourse, West Stand and also in the Matthew Harding Stand
Free commentaries for blind supporters are available
Contact: 0371 811-2012 (Bookings are necessary)

Travelling Supporters' Information:
Routes: From the North & East: Follow Central London signs from the A1/M1 to Hyde Park Corner, then signs for Guildford (A3) to Knightsbridge (A4). After 1 mile turn left into Fulham Road; From the South: Take the A13 or A24 then the A219 to cross Putney Bridge and follow signs for 'West End' (A304) to join the A308 into Fulham Road; From the West: Take the M4 then A4 to Central London, then follow signs to Westminster (A3220). After ¾ mile, turn right at crossroads into Fulham Road.

CHELTENHAM TOWN FC

Founded: 1887
Nickname: 'Robins'
Ground: Abbey Business Stadium, Whaddon Road, Cheltenham, Gloucestershire   GL52 5NA
Ground Capacity: 7,200
Seating Capacity: 4,054
Record Attendance: 8,326 (1956)

Pitch Size: 110 × 72 yards
Colours: Red and White striped shirts, Black shorts
Telephone Nº: (01242) 573558
Fax Number: (01242) 224675
Web Site: www.ctfc.com
E-mail: info@ctfc.com

GENERAL INFORMATION

Car Parking: Available at the ground for a £5.00 charge
Coach Parking: Please phone for details
Nearest Railway Station: Cheltenham Spa (2½ miles)
Nearest Bus Station: Cheltenham Royal Well
Club Shop: At the ground
Opening Times: Weekdays & Matchdays 10.00am–2.45pm.
Telephone Nº: (01242) 573558

GROUND INFORMATION

Away Supporters' Entrances & Sections:
Hazlewoods Stand (entrance from Whaddon Road) or the In2Print Stand

ADMISSION INFO (2017/2018 PRICES)

Adult Standing: £16.00
Adult Seating: £20.00 or £21.00
Junior/Student Standing: £5.00
Junior/Student Seating: £7.00
Concessionary Standing: £12.00
Concessionary Seating: £15.00
Programme Price: £3.00

FANS WITH DISABILITIES INFORMATION

Wheelchairs: Accommodated in front of the Main Stand (use main entrance) and in the In 2 Print Stand
Helpers: Admitted free of charge
Prices: Concessionary prices are charged
Disabled Toilets: Available in the In 2 Print Stand, adjacent to the Stagecoach West Stand and in the Social Club
Contact: (01242) 573558   (Bookings are necessary)

Travelling Supporters' Information:
Routes: The ground is situated to the North-East of Cheltenham, 1 mile from the Town Centre off the B4632 (Prestbury Road) – Whaddon Road is to the East of the B4632 just North of Pittville Circus. Road signs in the vicinity indicate 'Whaddon Road/Cheltenham Town FC'.

CHESTERFIELD FC

Founded: 1866 (**Entered League**: 1899)
Former Names: Chesterfield Municipal FC, Chesterfield Town FC
Nickname: 'Spireites' 'Blues'
Ground: Proact Stadium , 1866 Sheffield Road, Whittington Moor, Chesterfield   S41 8NZ
Ground Capacity: 10,300 (All seats)

Record Attendance: 30,968 (Saltergate – 7/4/1939)
Pitch Size: 112 × 71 yards
Colours: Blue shirts with White shorts
Telephone Nº: (01246) 269300
Fax Number: (01246) 556799
Web Site: www.chesterfield-fc.co.uk

GENERAL INFORMATION
Car Parking: Various Car Parks available nearby
Coach Parking: At the ground
Nearest Railway Station: Chesterfield (1¼ miles)
Nearest Bus Station: Chesterfield
Club Shop: At the ground
Opening Times: Monday to Friday 9.00am to 5.00pm. Saturday 10.00am to 3.00pm on matchdays only
Telephone Nº: (01246) 209765

GROUND INFORMATION
Away Supporters' Entrances & Sections:
North (Rubicon Stand) Turnstiles

ADMISSION INFO (2017/2018 PRICES)
Adult Seating: £20.00 – £26.00
Juvenile (Under-17s) Seating: £5.00 – £13.00
Concessionary Seating: £13.00 – £21.00
Under-7s Seating: £2.00 in the Family Stand
Note: Prices may vary depending on the category of the game
Programme Price: £3.00

FANS WITH DISABILITIES INFORMATION
Wheelchairs: Up to 100 spaces available around the ground
Note: Lifts are available in the East and West stands
Helpers: One helper admitted per fan with disabilities
Prices: Concessionary prices for fans with disabilities. One helper admitted free of charge with each fan.
Disabled Toilets: Available in all stands
Contact: (01246) 269300   (Bookings are advised)

Travelling Supporters' Information:
Routes: From the South: Exit the M1 at Junction 29 and follow the A617 for Chesterfield. At the roundabout, take the 4th exit and head north on the A61 Sheffield Road and the stadium is located in the Whittington Moor district next to the junction with the A619; From the East: Take the A619 to Chesterfield and the ground is situated next to the Tesco supermarket at the junction with the A61; From the North: Exit the M1 at Junction 30 and take the A619 to Chesterfield. Then as above.

COLCHESTER UNITED FC

Founded: 1937 (**Entered League**: 1950)
Former Names: The Eagles FC & Colchester Town FC
Nickname: 'U's'
Ground: Weston Homes Community Stadium, United Way, Colchester CO4 5UP
Ground Capacity: 10,105 (All seats)
Record Attendance: 19,072 (27/11/48 – Layer Road)
Pitch Size: 112 × 72 yards

Colours: Royal blue & white striped shirts with Royal blue shorts
Telephone Nº: (01206) 755100
Ticket Office: (01206) 755161
Fax Number: (01206) 755114
Web Site: www.cu-fc.com
E-mail: ticketing@colchesterunited.net

GENERAL INFORMATION

Car Parking: 700 spaces at the ground – pre-bookings only. The club recommends fans should use the Matchday shuttle bus service (cost £1.50) where possible. This runs from Bruff Close, near Colchester North Railway Station where there is a large car park for all fans.
Coach Parking: Drivers should liaise with with stewards upon arrival at the ground
Nearest Railway Station: Colchester North (1½ miles)
Nearest Bus Station: Colchester Town Centre (1½ miles)
Club Shop: At the ground
Opening Times: Matchdays only 10.00am to 3.00pm then 5.00pm to 6.00pm.
Telephone Nº: (01206) 755135

GROUND INFORMATION

Away Supporters' Entrances & Sections:
North Stand or East Stand (North End)

ADMISSION INFO (2017/2018 PRICES)

Adult Seating: £21.00 – £29.00
Concessionary Seating: £16.00 – £23.00
Ages 18 to 21 Seating: £17.00
Under-18s Seating: £13.00 – £16.00
Under-14s Seating: £5.00 – £8.00
Under-11s Seating: Free of charge
Note: A variety of discounted rates are available for tickets purchased a set number of weeks in advance of the game.
Programme Price: £3.00

FANS WITH DISABILITIES INFORMATION

Wheelchairs: 40 spaces in total situated in all stands with lift access available where required.
Helpers: One helper admitted per wheelchair
Prices: £13.00 – £23.00 for each adult fan with disabilities. Helpers are admitted free of charge.
Disabled Toilets: Available in each stand
Contact: (01206) 755161

Travelling Supporters' Information:
Routes: The stadium is located at junction 28 of the A12 on the northern outskirts of Colchester. As parking near the stadium is very limited, the club recommends both home and away fans should use the Matchday shuttle bus service which runs from Bruff Close, near to Colchester North Station where there is a large car park. Alternatively, pre-book a space in the club car park.

COVENTRY CITY FC

Founded: 1883   (**Entered League**: 1919)
Former Names: Singers FC (1883-1898)
Nickname: 'Sky Blues'
Ground: Ricoh Arena, Phoenix Way, Foleshill, Coventry   CV6 6GE
Ground Capacity: 32,400 (All seats)
Record Attendance: 51,455 (At Highfield Road)
Pitch Size: 110 × 74 yards

Colours: Sky Blue shirts and socks, White shorts
Telephone Nº: (024) 7699-1987
Ticket Office: (024) 7699-1987
Web Site: www.ccfc.co.uk
E-mail: info@ccfc.co.uk
Postal Address: Sky Blue Lodge, Leamington Road, Ryton-on-Dunsmore, Coventry   CV8 3FL

GENERAL INFORMATION

Car Parking: 2,000 spaces available at the ground. Please pre-book parking via www.ricoharena.com or the ticket office
Coach Parking: At the ground (Car Park 'C')
Nearest Railway Station: Coventry (3 miles)
Nearest Bus Station: Coventry (3 miles)
Club Shop: At the ground and in the City Centre
Opening Times: Weekday office hours and Matchdays
Telephone Nº: (024) 7767-2021

GROUND INFORMATION

Away Supporters' Entrances & Sections:
Turnstiles 1-11

ADMISSION INFO (2017/2018 PRICES)

Adult Seating: £24.00 – £26.00
Under-16s Seating: £5.00 (Members only)
Under-18s Seating: £12.00 – £13.00
Concessionary Seating: £17.00 – £18.00
Note: Tickets are cheaper when purchased in advance
Programme Price: £3.00

FANS WITH DISABILITIES INFORMATION

Wheelchairs: 94 spaces available in total
Helpers: Admitted
Prices: Normal prices apply for fans with disabilities. Free of charge for helpers
Disabled Toilets: Available
Contact: (024) 7699-2335 (Bookings are necessary)

Travelling Supporters' Information:
Routes: From All Parts: Exit the M6 at Junction 3 and follow the A444 towards Coventry. The ground is located just 400 yards along this road. Please note that parking spaces at the ground must be pre-booked. No street parking.

CRAWLEY TOWN FC

Founded: 1896 (**Entered League**: 2011)
Former Names: None
Nickname: 'Red Devils'
Ground: The Checkatrade.com Stadium, Winfield Way, Crawley, West Sussex   RH11 9RX
Record Attendance: 5,880 (2013)
Pitch Size: 113 × 72 yards

Colours: Red shirts and shorts
Telephone Nº: (01293) 410000 (Ground)
Ticket Office: (01293) 410005
Fax Number: (01293) 410002
Ground Capacity: 5,996   **Seating Capacity**: 3,295
Web site: www.crawleytownfc.com
E-mail: feedback@crawleytownfc.com

GENERAL INFORMATION

Car Parking: Free parking available within a 5 minute walk.
Coach Parking: At the ground
Nearest Railway Station: Crawley (1 mile)
Nearest Bus Station: By the Railway Station
Club Shop: At the ground
Opening Times: Weekdays 9.30am to 5.00pm; Saturday matches 12.00pm to 6.00pm; Mid-week matches 6.00pm to kick-off then for 30 minutes after the game
Telephone Nº: (01293) 410000

GROUND INFORMATION

Away Supporters' Entrances & Sections:
North Entrance for both terrace and seating

ADMISSION INFO (2016/2017 PRICES)

Adult Standing: £16.00 – £18.00
Adult Seating: £20.00 – £22.00
Under-18s Standing/Seating: £10.00
Under-16s Standing/Seating: £4.00
Under-11s Standing/Seating: £1.00
Senior Citizen Standing: £12.00 – £14.00
Senior Citizen Seating: £16.00 – £18.00
Programme Price: £3.00

FANS WITH DISABILITIES INFORMATION

Wheelchairs: Accommodated in a special section of the Main Stand (Lift access available)
Helpers: One helper admitted per fan with disabilities
Prices: Normal prices apply for fans with disabilities. Free of charge for helpers
Disabled Toilets: Available
Contact: (01293) 410000   (Bookings are necessary)

Travelling Supporters' Information:
Routes: Exit the M23 at Junction 11 and take the A23 towards Crawley. After ¼ mile, the Stadium is on the left. Take the first exit at the roundabout for the Stadium entrance.

CREWE ALEXANDRA FC

Founded: 1877 (**Entered League**: 1892)
Nickname: 'Railwaymen'
Ground: Alexandra Stadium, Gresty Road, Crewe, Cheshire   CW2 6EB
Ground Capacity: 10,107 (All seats)
Record Attendance: 20,000 (30th January 1960)
Pitch Size: 112 × 74 yards

Colours: Red shirts with White shorts
Telephone No: (01270) 213014
Ticket Office: (01270) 252610
Fax Number: (01270) 216320
Web Site: www.crewealex.net
E-mail: info@crewealex.net

GENERAL INFORMATION

Car Parking: Car Park at the ground (spaces for 400 cars)
Coach Parking: Car Park at the ground
Nearest Railway Station: Crewe (5 minutes walk)
Nearest Bus Station: Crewe Town
Club Shop: At the ground
Opening Times: Monday to Friday and Matchdays 9.00am – 5.00pm (until 7.45pm for Night matches)
Telephone No: (01270) 213014 extension 101

GROUND INFORMATION

Away Supporters' Entrances & Sections:
Popular Side Away Stand

ADMISSION INFO (2017/2018 PRICES)

Adult Seating: £20.00 – £22.00
Senior Citizen Seating: £15.50 – £17.00
Under-17s Seating: £9.50 – £10.50
Under-11s Seating: £6.00 – £6.50
Note: Members qualify for cheaper prices. Family tickets are available in the Family Stand.
Programme Price: £2.50

FANS WITH DISABILITIES INFORMATION

Wheelchairs: Over 70 spaces available in total for home and away fans around the ground
Helpers: One helper admitted per fan with disabilities
Prices: £17.00 for each fan with disabilities and one helper
Disabled Toilets: Available in all Stands
Commentaries are available for the blind
Contact: (01270) 252610 (Bookings are necessary)

Travelling Supporters' Information:
Routes: From the North: Exit the M6 at Junction 17 and take the Crewe (A534) road, and at Crewe roundabout follow signs for Chester into Nantwich Road. Then take a left turn into Gresty Road; From the South and East: Take the A52 to the A5020, then on to Crewe roundabout (then as from the North); From the West: Take the A534 into Crewe and turn right just before the railway station into Gresty Road.   **SatNav users**: Please enter the following post code: CW2 6EB

CRYSTAL PALACE FC

Photo courtesy of Crystal Palace FC

Founded: 1905 (**Entered League**: 1920)
Nickname: 'Eagles'
Ground: Selhurst Park, London   SE25 6PU
Ground Capacity: 25,850 (All seats)
Record Attendance: 51,482 (11th May 1979)
Pitch Size: 110 × 74 yards

Colours: Red and Blue striped shirts with Blue shorts
Telephone Nº: (020) 8768-6000
Ticket Office: 0871 200-0071
Fax Number: (020) 8771-5311
Web Site: www.cpfc.co.uk
E-mail: communications@cpfc.co.uk

GENERAL INFORMATION

Car Parking: Street Parking only
Coach Parking: Thornton Heath
Nearest Railway Station: Selhurst or Norwood Junction (both 5 minutes walk)
Nearest Bus Station: West Croydon
Club Shop: At the ground
Opening Times: Weekdays & Matchdays 8.30am to 5.00pm and Matchdays from 9.00am until 30 minutes after kick-off. Also open for 30 minutes after the final whistle.
Telephone Nº: (020) 8768-6100

GROUND INFORMATION

Away Supporters' Entrances & Sections:
Park Road for the Arthur Wait Stand

ADMISSION INFO (2017/2018 PRICES)

Adult Seating: £27.00 – £50.00
Concessionary Seating: £19.00 – £35.00
Junior Seating: £13.50 – £24.00
Note: Prices vary depending on the category of the game
Programme Price: £3.00

FANS WITH DISABILITIES INFORMATION

Wheelchairs: Spaces are available in a special area in the Holmesdale Road Stand and also in the Arthur Wait Stand
Helpers: One helper admitted per wheelchair
Prices: Normal prices apply for fans with disabilities. Helpers are admitted free of charge
Disabled Toilets: Located in the Holmesdale Road Stand Commentaries are available for 12 people
Contact: (020) 8768-6080   (Bookings are necessary)

Travelling Supporters' Information:
Routes: From the North: Take the M1/A1 to the North Circular (A406) for Chiswick. Take the South Circular (A205) to Wandsworth then the A3 to the A214 and follow signs for Streatham to the A23. Turn left onto the B273 after 1 mile, follow to the end, turn left into the High Street and then into Whitehorse Lane; From the East: Take the A232 (Croydon Road) to Shirley and join the A215 (Northwood Road). After 2¼ miles turn left into Whitehorse Lane; From the South: Take the A23 and follow signs for Crystal Palace (B266) through Thornton Heath into Whitehorse Lane; From the West: Take the M4 to Chiswick (then as North).

DERBY COUNTY FC

Founded: 1884 (**Entered League**: 1888)
Nickname: 'Rams'
Ground: The iPro Stadium, Pride Park, Royal Way,
Pride Park, Derby   DE24 8XL
Ground Capacity: 33,455 (All seats)
Record Attendance: 33,597 (25th May 2001)
Pitch Size: 110 × 74 yards

Colours: White shirts with Black shorts
Telephone Nº: 0871 472-1884
Ticket Office: 0871 472-1884   Option 1
Fax Number: (01332) 667519
Web Site: www.dcfc.co.uk
E-mail: derby.county@dcfc.co.uk

GENERAL INFORMATION

Car Parking: Spaces for 1,424 cars at the ground (available for permit holders only)
Coach Parking: At the ground
Nearest Railway Station: Derby (1 mile)
Nearest Bus Station: Derby Central
Club Shop: DCFC Megastore at the ground
Opening Times: Monday to Saturday 9.00am – 5.00pm (from 10.00am on Tuesdays); Sundays 10.00am – 4.00pm
Telephone Nº: 0871 472-1884 (Option 2)

GROUND INFORMATION

Away Supporters' Entrances & Sections:
South East Corner

ADMISSION INFO (2017/2018 PRICES)

Due to the introduction of a 'dynamic' pricing system, we suggest that fans contact the club for further details about admission prices for any particular game.
Programme Price: £3.00

FANS WITH DISABILITIES INFORMATION

Wheelchairs: 206 spaces available in total
Helpers: One helper admitted for each fan with disabilities
Prices: Please contact the club for further information
Disabled Toilets: Yes
Contact: (01332) 821044   (Bookings are necessary)

Travelling Supporters' Information:
Routes: From All Parts: Exit the M1 at Junction 25 and follow the A52 towards the City Centre until the ground is signposted on the left. Follow the signs for the ground.
From the Train Station: The Stadium is 10 minutes walk by way of a tunnel under the railway opposite Brunswick Inn, Station Approach. Then follow the footpath; Buses: A shuttle service runs from the bus station from 1.00pm until 2.45pm on Saturdays. A similar service runs from 6.00pm – 7.30pm for midweek games. Return shuttles are available post-match.

DONCASTER ROVERS FC

Founded: 1879
Former Names: None
Nickname: 'Rovers'
Ground: Keepmoat Stadium, Stadium Way, Doncaster   DN4 5JW
Record Attendance: 15,001 (1st April 2008)
Pitch Size: 110 × 72 yards

Colours: Red & White hooped shirts with Black shorts
Telephone Nº: (01302) 764664
Ticket Office: (01302) 762576
Fax Number: (01302) 363525
Ground Capacity: 15,126 (All seats)
Web site: www.doncasterroversfc.co.uk
E-mail: info@clubdoncaster.co.uk

GENERAL INFORMATION

Car Parking: 1,000 spaces available at the ground
Coach Parking: At the ground
Nearest Railway Station: Doncaster (2 miles)
Nearest Bus Station: Doncaster (2 miles)
Club Shop: At the ground
Opening Times: 10.00am to 4.30pm on weekdays and 10.00am to 4.00pm on Saturdays
Telephone Nº: (01302) 764664

GROUND INFORMATION

Away Supporters' Entrances & Sections:
North Stand

ADMISSION INFO (2017/2018 PRICES)

Adult Seating: £21.00 – £22.00
Concessionary Seating: £17.00 – £18.00
Ages 17 to 21 Seating: £13.00 – £14.00
Ages 12 to 16 Seating: £8.00
Under-12s Seating: £5.00
Note: Members prices are lower than those shown.
Programme Price: £3.00

FANS WITH DISABILITIES INFORMATION

Wheelchairs: Accommodated throughout the ground (Away fans accommodated in the North Stand)
Helpers: Admitted
Prices: Normal prices for fans with disabilities. Helpers are admitted free of charge
Disabled Toilets: Available in all Stands
Contact: (01302) 764664   (Bookings are necessary)

Travelling Supporters' Information:
Routes: Exit the M18 at Junction 3 and follow the A6182 towards Doncaster. The stadium is approximately 1½ miles from the motorway and is well signposted so follow these signs. There are 1,000 car parking spaces available at the stadium and the cost is £5.00 per car. A number of businesses on the nearby business park also offer matchday parking for a similar charge.
Bus services run from the town centre/interchange to the Stadium with a shuttle service back operating after the match.

EVERTON FC

Founded: 1878 (**Entered League**: 1888)
Former Names: St. Domingo's FC (1878-79)
Nickname: 'The Toffees'
Ground: Goodison Park, Goodison Road, Liverpool L4 4EL
Ground Capacity: 39,571 (All seats)
Record Attendance: 78,299 (18th September 1948)

Pitch Size: 110 × 74 yards
Colours: Blue shirts with White shorts
Telephone Nº: (0151) 556-1878
Ticket Office: (0151) 556-1878
Fax Number: (0151) 213-0446
Web Site: www.evertonfc.com
E-mail: everton@evertonfc.com

GENERAL INFORMATION

Car Parking: Corner of Priory Road and Utting Avenue
Coach Parking: Priory Road
Nearest Railway Station: Kirkdale
Nearest Mainline Railway Station: Liverpool Lime Street
Nearest Bus Station: Queen's Square, Liverpool
Club Shop: 'Megastore' in Walton Lane by the ground
Opening Times: Weekdays 9.30am to 5.00pm, Saturdays 9.00am to 5.00pm and Sundays 11.00am to 3.00pm
Telephone Nº: (0151) 556-1878

GROUND INFORMATION

Away Supporters' Entrances & Sections:
Bullens Road entrances for Bullens Stand – Turnstiles 55-60

ADMISSION INFO (2017/2018 PRICES)

Adult Seating: £38.00 – £49.00
Junior Seating: £19.00 – £24.00
Senior Citizen Seating: £26.00 – £32.00
Note: Concessionary prices are only available in some areas and prices vary depending on the category of the game

FANS WITH DISABILITIES INFORMATION

Wheelchairs: 85 spaces for home fans, 13 spaces for away fans in a special section.
Helpers: One helper admitted per wheelchair
Prices: Normal prices for fans with disabilities. Helpers free of charge
Disabled Toilets: Available in the section for disabled fans. Commentaries are available for the blind
Contact: (0151) 556-1878 (Bookings are necessary)

Travelling Supporters' Information:
Routes: From the North: Exit the M6 at Junction 26 onto the M58 and continue to it's end. Take the 2nd exit at the roundabout onto the A59 Ormskirk Road. Continue along into Rice Lane and go straight across at the next roundabout into County Road. After ½ mile, turn left into Everton Valley then bear left into Walton Lane for the ground; From the South & East: Exit the M6 at Junction 21A and take the M62 to it's end. Turn right at traffic lights onto A5088 Queen Drive and continue to the junction with Walton Hall Avenue then turn left into Walton Lane (A580) and the ground is on the right.
Bus Services: Services to the ground – 19, 20, F1, F2, 30

EXETER CITY FC

Founded: 1901   (**Re-Entered League**: 2008)
Former Names: Formed by the amalgamation of
St. Sidwell United FC & Exeter United FC
Nickname: 'The Grecians'
Ground: St. James Park, Exeter, EX4 6PX
Ground Capacity: 8,541   (lower at present due to
Seating Capacity: 3,517   ongoing redevelopment)
Record Attendance: 21,014 (4th March 1931)

Pitch Size: 114 × 73 yards
Colours: Red and White striped shirts, Black shorts
Telephone Nº: (01392) 411243
Ticket Office: (01392) 411243
Fax Number: (01392) 413959
Web Site: www.exetercityfc.co.uk
E-mail: reception@ecfc.co.uk

GENERAL INFORMATION

Car Parking: Parr Street, John Lewis and Bampfyled Street
car parks
Coach Parking: Paris Street Bus Station (10 minute walk)
Nearest Railway Station: Exeter St. James Park (adjacent)
Nearest Bus Station: Paris Street Bus Station
Club Shop: At the ground
Opening Times: Monday to Friday 8.30am to 5.00pm and
11.00am to 5.00pm on matchdays.
Club Shop Telephone Nº: (01392) 425885

GROUND INFORMATION

Away Supporters' Entrances & Sections:
St. James Road turnstiles for standing in the St. James Road
End and access to seating in the Main Stand
Note: Cash is only taken on the Thatcher Gold Big Bank
turnstiles. Away section tickets are sold at the booth adjacent
to the St. James Road turnstiles.

ADMISSION INFO (2017/2018 PRICES)

Adult Standing: £17.00
Adult Seating: £23.00
Concessionary Standing: £13.00
Concessionary Seating: £19.00 – £21.00
Under-18s Standing: £5.00 **Seating**: £6.00 – £10.00
Programme Price: £3.00

FANS WITH DISABILITIES INFORMATION

Wheelchairs: Accommodated in the IP Office Main Stand
and the Big Bank.
Helpers: One assistant admitted per wheelchair
Prices: Free of charge for assistants. £13.00 – £21.00 for
fans with disabilities
Disabled Toilets: Available by the Big Bank Stand
Contact: (01392) 411243   (Bookings are necessary)

Travelling Supporters' Information:
Routes: From the North: Exit the M5 at Junction 29 and follow signs to the City Centre along Heavitree Road. Take the 4th exit
at the roundabout into Western Way and the 2nd exit into Tiverton Road then 2nd left into Stadium Way; From the East: Take
the A30 into Heavitree Road (then as from the North); From the South & West: Take the A38 and follow City Centre signs into
Western Way, then take the third exit at the roundabout into St. James Road.   (Follow the brown football signs from the M5)
Note: This ground is difficult to find being in a residential area on the side of a hill without prominent floodlights!

FLEETWOOD TOWN FC

Founded: 1997   (**Entered League**: 2012)
Former Names: Fleetwood FC (1908-1976),
Fleetwood Town FC (1977-1996), Fleetwood
Freeport FC (1997-2002)
Nickname: 'Cod Army'
Ground: Highbury Stadium, Park Avenue,
Fleetwood   FY7 6TX
Record Attendance: 5,092 vs Blackpool FC (2012)
Pitch Size: 110 × 71 yards

Colours: Red shirts with White Arms, White shorts
Telephone Nº: (01253) 775080
Fax Number: (01253) 775081
Ground Capacity: 5,280
Seating Capacity: 2,670
Web site: www.fleetwoodtownfc.com
E-mail: info@fleetwoodtownfc.com

GENERAL INFORMATION

Car Parking: Street parking only
Coach Parking: Contact the club for information
Nearest Railway Station: Poulton-le-Fylde (7 miles)
Nearest Bus Station: None
Nearest Tram Stop from Blackpool: Stanley Road
Club Shop: At the ground
Opening Times: Monday to Friday 9.00am to 5.00pm
Telephone Nº: (01253) 775080

GROUND INFORMATION

Away Supporters' Entrances & Sections:
Standing in the Percy Ronson stand and seating in the
Parkside Stand

ADMISSION INFO (2017/2018 PRICES)

Adult Standing: £22.00   **Adult Seating**: £23.00–£29.00
Under-18s Standing: £10.00
Under-18s Seating: £11.00 – £17.00
Under-16s Standing: £5.00
Under-16s Seating: £6.00 – £12.00
Senior Citizen Standing: £17.00
Senior Citizen Seating: £18.00 – £24.00
Note: Prices are cheaper for members

FANS WITH DISABILITIES INFORMATION

Wheelchairs: Accommodated
Helpers: Admitted
Prices: Normal prices for the fans with disabilities. Free of
charge for helpers
Disabled Toilets: Available
Contact: (01253) 775080   (Bookings are necessary)

Travelling Supporters' Information:
Routes: Exit the M6 at Junction 32 and take the M55 towards Blackpool. Exit the M55 at Junction 3 and follow the A585
towards Fleetwood for approximately 11½ miles. On the outskirts of town, you will reach a roundabout with Blackpool and
Fylde college on your left. Continue straight on at this roundabout but then take the first turn on the left into Copse Road. After
approximately 1 mile, branch left and turn left onto Radcliffe Road as you pass the Fire Station. Take the next right onto Stanley
Road and the Stadium is at the bottom of the road on the left.

FOREST GREEN ROVERS FC

Founded: 1889   (**Entered League**: 2017)
Former Names: Stroud FC
Nickname: 'The Green Devils'
Ground: The New Lawn, Another Way,
Forest Green, Nailsworth, Gloucestershire, GL6 0FG
Record Attendance: 4,836 (3rd January 2009)
Pitch Size: 110 × 70 yards

Colours: Black and White striped shirts, Black shorts
Telephone Nº: (01453) 834860
Fax Number: (01453) 835291
Ground Capacity: 5,025
Seating Capacity: 1,881
Web site: www.forestgreenroversfc.com
E-mail: reception@forestgreenroversfc.com

GENERAL INFORMATION

Car Parking: At the ground
Coach Parking: At the ground
Nearest Railway Station: Stroud (4 miles)
Nearest Bus Station: Nailsworth
Club Shop: At the ground
Opening Times: Monday to Friday 9.00am to 3.00pm
Telephone Nº: (01453) 834860

GROUND INFORMATION

Away Supporters' Entrances & Sections:
EESI Stand

ADMISSION INFO (2017/2018 PRICES)

Adult Standing: £18.00   **Adult Seating**: £21.00–£23.00
Senior Citizen Standing: £14.00
Senior Citizen Seating: £17.00 – £19.00
Under-11s Standing/Seating: Free of charge – £4.00
Young Adult Standing: £9.00
Young Adult Seating: £11.00 – £13.00
Note: Discounted prices are available for advance purchases

FANS WITH DISABILITIES INFORMATION

Wheelchairs: Accommodated in the Main Stand
Helpers: Admitted
Prices: Normal prices for fans with disabilities. Helpers free
Disabled Toilets: Available
Contact: (01453) 834860   (Enquiries are required at least 72 hours in advance of the game)

Travelling Supporters' Information:
Routes: The ground is located 4 miles south of Stroud on the A46 to Bath. Upon entering Nailsworth, turn into Spring Hill at the mini-roundabout and the ground is approximately ½ mile up the hill on the left.

FULHAM FC

Founded: 1879 (**Entered League**: 1907)
Former Names: Fulham St. Andrew's FC (1879-1898)
Nickname: 'The Whites'
Ground: Craven Cottage, Stevenage Road, Fulham, London   SW6 6HH
Ground Capacity: 25,700 (All seats)
Record Attendance: 49,335 (8th October 1938)

Pitch Size: 109 × 71 yards
Colours: White shirts with Black shorts
Telephone Nº: 0843 208-1222
Ticket Office: 0843 208-1234
Fax Number: 0870 442-0236
Web Site: www.fulhamfc.com
E-mail: enquiries@fulhamfc.com

GENERAL INFORMATION
Car Parking: Street Parking (Matchday restrictions apply)
Coach Parking: Stevenage Road/Fulham Palace Road
Nearest Railway Station: Putney (1 mile)
Nearest Tube Station: Putney Bridge (District) (1 mile)
Club Shop: At the ground
Opening Times: At the ground: Monday to Saturday 9.00am to 5.00pm and Sundays 11.00am to 4.00pm
Telephone Nº: 0843 208-1223

GROUND INFORMATION
Away Supporters' Entrances & Sections:
Putney End for the Putney Stand

ADMISSION INFO (2017/2018 PRICES)
Adult Seating: £25.00 – £45.00
Junior Seating: £15.00 – £25.00
Concessionary Seating: £20.00 – £40.00
Note: Prices vary depending on the category of the game and tickets purchased in advance are cheaper.
Programme Price: £3.50

FANS WITH DISABILITIES INFORMATION
Wheelchairs: 31 spaces for Home fans and 9 spaces for Away fans in the Putney End, Block 7
Helpers: One assistant admitted per fan with disabilities
Prices: Half-price for fans with disabilities. One helper admitted free of charge for each fan in a wheelchair.
Disabled Toilets: Available
Contact: 0843 208-1234   (Bookings necessary)

Travelling Supporters' Information:
Routes: From the North: Take the A1/M1 to the North Circular (A406), travel west to Neasden and follow signs for Harlesden A404, then Hammersmith A219. At Broadway, follow the Fulham sign and turn right after 1 mile into Harbord Street then left at the end for the ground; From the South & East: Take the South Circular (A205), follow the Putney Bridge sign (A219). Cross the bridge and follow Hammersmith signs for ½ mile, turn left into Bishops Park Road, then right at the end; From the West: Take the M4 to the A4. Branch left after 2 miles into Hammersmith Broadway (then as from the North).

GILLINGHAM FC

Founded: 1893 (**Entered League**: 1920)
Former Names: New Brompton FC (1893-1913)
Nickname: 'Gills'
Ground: Priestfield Stadium, Redfern Avenue,
Gillingham, Kent   ME7 4DD
Ground Capacity: 11,440 (All seats)
Record Attendance: 23,002 (10th January 1948)

Pitch Size: 110 × 70 yards
Telephone Nº: (01634) 300000
Ticket Office: (01634) 300000
Fax Number: (01634) 850986
Web Site: www.gillinghamfootballclub.com
E-mail: enquiries@priestfield.com

GENERAL INFORMATION

Car Parking: Street parking
Coach Parking: By Police direction
Nearest Railway Station: Gillingham
Nearest Bus Station: Gillingham
Club Shop: Megastore in Redfern Avenue
Opening Times: Megastore is open Weekdays from 9.00am to 5.00pm and Matchdays from 9.00am to 3.00pm
Telephone Nº: (01634) 300000

GROUND INFORMATION

Away Supporters' Entrances & Sections:
Priestfield Road End

ADMISSION INFO (2017/2018 PRICES)

Adult Seating: £22.00 – £25.00
Senior Citizen Seating: £19.00 – £21.00
Under-18s Seating: £7.00 – £9.00
Under-12s Seating: £7.00 – £9.00
Note: Tickets are £2.00 more if purchased on the matchday
Programme Price: £3.00

FANS WITH DISABILITIES INFORMATION

Wheelchairs: 65 spaces in total for Home and Away fans and helpers in special sections around the ground
Helpers: One helper admitted per fan with disabilities
Prices: Normal prices for fans with disabilities. Helpers free
Disabled Toilets: Available in the Gordon Road Stand
Contact: (01634) 300000   (Bookings are necessary)

Travelling Supporters' Information:
Routes: From All Parts: Exit the M2 at Junction 4 and follow the link road (dual carriageway) B278 to the 3rd roundabout. Turn left onto the A2 (dual carriageway) and go across the roundabout to the traffic lights. Turn right into Woodlands Road after the traffic lights. The ground is ¼ mile on the left.

GRIMSBY TOWN FC

Founded: 1878
Former Names: Grimsby Pelham FC (1879)
Nickname: 'Mariners'
Ground: Blundell Park, Cleethorpes   DN35 7PY
Ground Capacity: 8,974 (All seats)
Record Attendance: 31,651 (20th February 1937)
Pitch Size: 111 × 74 yards

Colours: Black and White striped shirts, Black shorts
Telephone Nº: (01472) 605050
Ticket Office: (01472) 605050 (Option 4)
Fax Number: (01472) 693665
Web Site: www.grimsby-townfc.co.uk
E-mail: info@gtfc.co.uk

GENERAL INFORMATION

Car Parking: Street parking
Coach Parking: Harrington Street – near the ground
Nearest Railway Station: Cleethorpes (1½ miles)
Nearest Bus Station: Brighowgate, Grimsby (4 miles)
Club Shop: At the ground
Opening Times: Monday – Friday 9.00am to 5.00pm;
Matchday Saturdays 9.00am to kick-off
Telephone Nº: (01472) 605050

GROUND INFORMATION

Away Supporters' Entrances & Sections:
Harrington Street turnstiles 15-18 and Constitution Avenue turnstiles 5-14

ADMISSION INFO (2017/2018 PRICES)

Adult Seating: £20.00
Senior Citizen/Student Seating: £13.00
Young Adults Seating (Ages 15–18): £13.00
Child Seating: £5.00 – £7.00 (Under-15s)
Note: Tickets are cheaper if purchased before the matchday

FANS WITH DISABILITIES INFORMATION

Wheelchairs: 50 spaces in total for Home and Away fans in a special section in front of the Main Stand
Helpers: Helpers are admitted
Prices: £20.00 for fans with disabilities. Free for helpers
Disabled Toilets: Available
Commentaries are also available
Contact: (01472) 605050 (Bookings are necessary)

Travelling Supporters' Information:
Routes: From All Parts except Lincolnshire and East Anglia: Take the M180 to the A180 and follow signs for Grimsby/Cleethorpes. The A180 ends at a roundabout (the 3rd in short distance after crossing docks), take the 2nd exit from the roundabout over the Railway flyover into Cleethorpes Road (A1098) and continue into Grimsby Road. After the second stretch of dual carriageway, the ground is ½ mile on the left; From Lincolnshire: Take the A46 or A16 and follow Cleethorpes signs along (A1098) Weelsby Road for 2 miles. Take the 1st exit at the roundabout at the end of Clee Road into Grimsby Road. The ground is 1¾ miles on the right.

HUDDERSFIELD TOWN FC

Founded: 1908 (**Entered League**: 1910)
Nickname: 'Terriers'
Ground: The John Smith's Stadium, Huddersfield, HD1 6PX
Ground Capacity: 24,554 (All seats)
Record Attendance: 23,678 (12th December 1999)
Pitch Size: 115 × 76 yards

Colours: Blue and White striped shirts, White shorts and Black socks
Telephone Nº: (01484) 484112
Ticket Office: (01484) 484123
Fax Number: (01484) 484101
Web Site: www.htafc.com
E-mail: info@htafc.com

GENERAL INFORMATION

Car Parking: Car park for 1,100 cars adjacent (pre-sold)
Coach Parking: Adjacent car park
Nearest Railway Station: Huddersfield (1¼ miles)
Nearest Bus Station: Huddersfield
Club Shop: At the ground and in the Town Centre
Opening Times: Weekdays 9.00am to 5.00pm, Saturday Matchdays 9.00am to 3.00pm and Saturday Non-matchdays 9.00am to 12.00pm
Telephone Nº: (01484) 484144 or 430192

GROUND INFORMATION

Away Supporters' Entrances & Sections:
Chadwick Lawrence Stand

ADMISSION INFO (2017/2018 PRICES)

The club has sold over 20,000 season tickets for the 2017/18 season, the club's first in the Premier League, so very few tickets will be available for purchase. Please contact the club directly for further information about pricing and availability.
Programme Price: £3.00

FANS WITH DISABILITIES INFORMATION

Wheelchairs: 254 spaces in total for home and away fans in the special sections in the Chadwick Lawrence Stand, Revell Ward Stand and Britannia Rescue Stand. Additional spaces are available for the ambulant and visually impaired.
Helpers: Admitted
Prices: Please contact the club for details
Disabled Toilets: Available in the each of the sections Commentaries are available for the blind.
Contact: (01484) 484123 (Bookings are necessary)

Travelling Supporters' Information:
Routes: From the North, East and West: Exit the M62 at Junction 25 and take the A644 and A62 following Huddersfield signs. Follow signs for the Galpharm Stadium; From the South: Leave the M1 at Junction 38 and follow the A637/A642 to Huddersfield. At the Ring Road, follow signs for the A62 to the Galpharm Stadium.

HULL CITY AFC

Founded: 1904 (**Entered League**: 1905)
Nickname: 'Tigers'
Ground: KC Stadium, The Circle, Walton Street, Hull HU3 6HU
Ground Capacity: 25,586 (All seats)
Record Attendance: 24,945 (24th May 2009)
Pitch Size: 115 × 75 yards

Colours: Black and Amber shirts with Black shorts
Telephone Nº: (01482) 504600
Ticket Office: (01482) 505600
Fax Number: (01482) 304882
Web Site: www.hullcitytigers.com

GENERAL INFORMATION

Car Parking: Walton Street Car Park (£5.00), City Centre Car Parks and a Park & Ride scheme from Priory Park (£1.20)
Coach Parking: By Police direction
Nearest Railway Station: Hull Interchange
Nearest Bus Station: City Centre, Hull
Club Shop: Tiger Leisure Superstore at the Stadium
Opening Times: Monday to Saturday 9.00am to 5.00pm. Open until 5.30pm on Saturday matchdays
Telephone Nº: (01482) 509600

GROUND INFORMATION

Away Supporters' Entrances & Sections:
North Stand

ADMISSION INFO (2017/2018 PRICES)

Prices had not been set for the 2017/2018 season when we went to print. Please contact the club for pricing information.

FANS WITH DISABILITIES INFORMATION

Wheelchairs: 304 spaces in total for Home and Away fans available around all the stands at both upper and lower level
Helpers: One helper admitted per fan with disabilities (subject to registration)
Prices: Concessionary rates for fans with disabilities. Free of charge for helpers
Disabled Toilets: Available throughout the ground.
Lifts are available. Commentaries are available for the blind
Contact: (01482) 504600 (Bookings are not necessary)

Travelling Supporters' Information:
Routes: From the West: Take the M62 then join the A63. Continue under the Humber Bridge as the road becomes the A63 Clive Sullivan Way and turn off at the slip road just before the flyover marked "Local Traffic/Infirmary". Take the 2nd exit at the roundabout into Rawling Way. Turn left at the next main set of traffic lights on A1105 Anlaby Road. Continue over the flyover then take a right turn into Walton Street. The car park is half way down this street after the Sports Arena; From the Humber Bridge: Follow signs for Hull City Centre – the road curves round to the left to join the A63 Clive Sullivan Way. Then as from the West; From the North: Take the A1079 towards Beverley then follow signs for the Humber Bridge and A164. Take the A63 sign-posted Hull City Centre and follow onto the A63 Clive Sullivan Way. Then as from the West.

IPSWICH TOWN FC

Founded: 1878 (**Entered League**: 1938)
Nickname: 'Town' 'Tractor Boys'
Ground: Portman Road, Ipswich   IP1 2DA
Ground Capacity: 30,311 (All seats)
Record Attendance: 38,010 (8th March 1975)
Pitch Size: 110 × 72 yards

Colours: Blue shirts with White shorts
Telephone Nº: (01473) 400500
Ticket Office: 03330 05 05 03
Fax Number: (01473) 400040
Web Site: www.itfc.co.uk
E-mail: enquiries@itfc.co.uk

GENERAL INFORMATION

Car Parking: Portman Road & Sir Alf Ramsey Way car parks
Coach Parking: Bibb Way
Nearest Railway Station: Ipswich (5 minutes walk)
Nearest Bus Station: Ipswich
Club Shop: At the ground
Opening Times: Weekdays 9.00am–5.00pm. Opening times on Matchdays vary. Please contact the club for details
Telephone Nº: (01473) 400501

GROUND INFORMATION

Away Supporters' Entrances & Sections:
Cobbold Stand

ADMISSION INFO (2017/2018 PRICES)

Adult Seating: £25.00 – £52.00
Child Seating: £3.00 – £38.00
Senior Citizen Seating: £18.00 – £46.00
Programme Price: £3.00

FANS WITH DISABILITIES INFORMATION

Wheelchairs: 103 spaces and 103 seats for home fans in the East of England Cooperative, South and North Stands upper and lower tiers. 10 spaces and 10 seats for away fans in the lower East of England Cooperative Stand only.
Helpers: One helper admitted per fan with disabilities
Prices: Adult price charged for each fan with disabilities plus one helper.
Disabled Toilets: Available around the ground
Commentaries are available for the blind
Contact: 03330 05 05 03   (Bookings are necessary)

Travelling Supporters' Information:
Routes: From the North and West: Take the A1214 from the A14/A12 following signs for Ipswich West only. Proceed through Holiday Inn Hotel traffic lights and at the 3rd set of traffic lights turn right into West End Road. The ground is ¼ mile along on the left; From the South: Follow signs for Ipswich West, then as from the North and West above.

LEEDS UNITED FC

Founded: 1919 (**Entered League**: 1920)
Former Names: Formed after Leeds City FC were wound up for 'Irregular Practices'
Nickname: 'United'
Ground: Elland Road, Leeds LS11 0ES
Ground Capacity: 39,460 (All seats)
Record Attendance: 57,892 (15th March 1967)

Pitch Size: 115 × 74 yards
Colours: White shirts and shorts
Telephone Nº: 0871 334-1919
Ticket Office: 0871 334-1992
Fax Number: (0113) 367-6050
Web Site: www.leedsunited.com
E-mail: reception@leedsunited.com

GENERAL INFORMATION

Car Parking: Large car parks adjacent to the Stadium
Coach Parking: Adjacent to the Stadium
Nearest Railway Station: Leeds City (1½ miles)
Nearest Bus Station: Leeds City Centre – specials from Swinegate
Club Shop: At the South East corner of the Stadium
Opening Times: Weekdays 9.00am to 5.00pm, Matchdays 9.00am to one hour after the final whistle
Telephone Nº: 0871 334-1919 (Option 5)

GROUND INFORMATION

Away Supporters' Entrances & Sections:
South East Corner or South Stand – Upper & Lower Tiers

ADMISSION INFO (2017/2018 PRICES)

Adult Seating: £26.00 – £49.00
Concessionary Seating: £21.00 – £34.00
Under-16s Seating: £10.00 – £20.00
Under-11s Seating: £5.00 – £10.00
Note: Prices vary according to the category of game played and discounted prices are available for advance purchases.

FANS WITH DISABILITIES INFORMATION

Wheelchairs: 131 spaces in total in special sections in the West, North and South Stands
Helpers: One helper admitted per fan with disabilities
Prices: Please contact the club for details
Disabled Toilets: Available around the ground
Commentaries via headphones in the West Stand
Contact: (0113) 367-6178 (Ms. Tracey Lazenby)
(Bookings are necessary)

Travelling Supporters' Information:
Routes: From the North: Take the A58 or A61 into the City Centre and follow signs to the M621. Leave the Motorway after 1½ miles and exit the roundabout onto the A643 into Elland Road; From the North-East: Take the A63 or A64 into the City Centre (then as from the North); From the South: Take the M1 to the M621 (then as from the North); From the West: Take the M62 to the M621 (then as from the North).

LEICESTER CITY FC

Founded: 1884 (**Entered League**: 1894)
Former Names: Leicester Fosse FC (1884-1919)
Nickname: 'Foxes'
Ground: King Power Stadium, Filbert Way, Leicester, LE2 7FL
Ground Capacity: 32,500 (All seats)
Record Attendance: 32,148 (26th December 2003)

Pitch Size: 110 × 72 yards
Colours: Blue shirts with White shorts
Telephone Nº: 0344 815-5000
Ticket Office: 0344 815-5000 (Option 1)
Fax Number: (0116) 229-4404
Web Site: www.lcfc.com

GENERAL INFORMATION

Car Parking: NCP Car Park (5 minutes walk)
Coach Parking: Sawday Street
Nearest Railway Station: Leicester (1 mile)
Nearest Bus Station: St. Margaret's (1 mile)
Club Shop: At the ground
Opening Times: Monday to Saturday 9.00am–5.00pm.
Saturday Matchdays open 9.00am until kick-off then for 30
minutes after the game. Sundays open 10.00am – 4.00pm
Telephone Nº: 0344 815-5000 Option 7

GROUND INFORMATION

Away Supporters' Entrances & Sections:
At the corner of the North and East Stands

ADMISSION INFO (2016/2017 PRICES)

Adult Seating: £22.00 – £50.00
Under-22s Seating: £14.00 – £44.00
Under-18s Seating: £14.00 – £34.00
Under-12s Seating: Vary from free to £15.00 depending
on age and the category of the game.
Senior Citizen Seating: £22.00 – £44.00
Note: Prices vary depending on the category of the game.
Programme Price: £3.00

FANS WITH DISABILITIES INFORMATION

Wheelchairs: 186 spaces for wheelchairs plus 111 spaces
for helpers accommodated at various levels in all stands
Helpers: One carer admitted per fan with disabilities
Prices: Reduced prices are available – Phone for details
Disabled Toilets: Available in all stands
Contact: 0344 815-5000 (Hayley Mason – phone or fax)

Travelling Supporters' Information:
Routes: From the North: Take the A46/A607 into the City Centre or exit the M1 at Junction 21, take the A5460, turn right ¾
mile after the Railway Bridge into Upperton Road, then right into Filbert Way; From the East: Take the A47 into the City Centre
(then as from the North); From the South: Exit the M1 at Junction 21 and take the A5460, turn right ¾ mile after Railway
Bridge into Upperton Road, then right into Filbert Way; From the West: Take the M69 to the City Centre (then as from North).

LINCOLN CITY FC

Founded: 1884 (**Re-entered League**: 2017)
Nickname: 'Red Imps'
Ground: Sincil Bank Stadium, Lincoln   LN5 8LD
Ground Capacity: 10,120 (All seats)
Record Attendance: 23,196 (15th November 1967)
Pitch Size: 110 × 72 yards

Colours: Red and White striped shirts, Black shorts
Telephone Nº: (01522) 880011
Ticket Office: (01522) 880011
Fax Number: (01522) 880020
Web Site: www.redimps.co.uk
E-mail: info@lincolncityfc.co.uk

GENERAL INFORMATION

Car Parking: Stacey West Car Park (limited parking for £5.00 per car).
Coach Parking: Please contact the club for details.
Nearest Railway Station: Lincoln Central
Club Shop: At the ground
Opening Times: Weekdays 10.00am to 2.00pm and Saturday Matchdays 10.00am until kick-off and 30 minutes after the final whistle
Telephone Nº: (01522) 880011

GROUND INFORMATION

Away Supporters' Entrances & Sections:
Lincolnshire Co-operative Stand (seated) – Turnstiles 24 & 25

ADMISSION INFO (2017/2018 PRICES)

Adult Seating: £20.00
Junior/Junior Seating: £8.00
Concessionary Seating: £15.00
Note: Discounts are available for families and for advance ticket purchases

FANS WITH DISABILITIES INFORMATION

Wheelchairs: Limited number of spaces available in a special section adjacent to turnstile 23
Helpers: One helper admitted per fan with disabilities
Prices: Applications must be made to the club. Wheelchair-bound fans are charged concessionary prices. Helpers are admitted free if the fan they are assisting receives a medium/high level disability allowance
Disabled Toilets: Available
Contact: (01522) 880011   (Bookings are necessary)

Travelling Supporters' Information:
Routes: From the East: Take the A46 or A158 into the City Centre following Newark (A46) signs into the High Street and take next left (Scorer Street and Cross Street) for the ground; From the North and West: Take the A15 or A57 into the City Centre, then as from the East; From the South: Take the A1 then A46 for the City Centre, then into the High Street, parking on the South Common or in the Stadium via South Park Avenue, turn down by the Fire Station.

LIVERPOOL FC

Founded: 1892 (**Entered League**: 1893)
Nickname: 'Reds'
Ground: Anfield Road, Liverpool L4 0TH
Ground Capacity: 54,000 (All seats)
Record Attendance: 61,905 (2nd February 1952)
Pitch Size: 111 × 74 yards

Colours: Red shirts, shorts and socks
Telephone Nº: (0151) 264-2500
Ticket Office: 0843 170-5555
Ticket Office Fax Number: (0151) 261-1416
Customer Services: 0843 170-5000
Web Site: www.liverpoolfc.com

GENERAL INFORMATION

Car Parking: None available in the immediate area
Coach Parking: Priory Road and Pinehurst Avenue
Nearest Railway Station: Kirkdale (¾ mile)
Nearest Bus Station: Paradise Street, Liverpool
Club Shop: At the ground, at Williamson Square and
'Liverpool One' in the City Centre and in Chester City Centre
Opening Times: At Anfield: Monday to Friday 9.00am to
5.00pm, Saturdays 9.30am to 4.00pm; At Williamson Square
and Chester: Monday to Friday 9.00am to 5.30pm;
At Liverpool One: Monday to Friday 9.30am to 8.00pm,
Saturdays 9.00am – 7.00pm and Sundays 11.00am – 5.00pm
Telephone Nº: (0151) 263-2361

GROUND INFORMATION

Away Supporters' Entrances & Sections:
Anfield Road

ADMISSION INFO (2017/2018 PRICES)

Adult Seating: £37.00 – £59.00
Senior Citizen Seating: £28.00 – £44.00
Young Adult Seating: £18.50 – £29.50
Junior Seating: £9.00
Programme Price: £3.00

FANS WITH DISABILITIES INFORMATION

Wheelchairs: 100 spaces are available in total in the
Paddock Enclosure, Kop Stand and Anfield Road Stand.
8 of these spaces are reserved for away fans.
Helpers: One helper is admitted per wheelchair but a
second helper can sometimes be accommodated
Prices: £28.00 for fans with disabilities. One helper is
admitted free of charge with each fan with disabilities.
Disabled Toilets: Two available in the Paddock, two in the
Kop Stand and one in the Anfield Road Stand
Commentaries are available for the visually impaired on request
Contact: (0151) 264-2500 Option 2 (Bookings are necessary)
E-mail: disability@liverpoolfc.com

Travelling Supporters' Information:
Routes: From the North: Exit the M6 at Junction 28 and follow Liverpool A580 signs into Walton Hall Avenue, pass Stanley
Park and turn left into Anfield Road; From the South and East: Take the M62 to the end of the motorway, then turn right into
Queen's Drive (A5058) and turn left after 3 miles into Utting Avenue. After 1 mile, turn right into Anfield Road; From North
Wales: Take the Mersey Tunnel into the City Centre and follow signs for Preston (A580) into Walton Hall Avenue. Turn right into
Anfield Road before Stanley Park.

LUTON TOWN FC

Founded: 1885 (**Re-entered League**: 2014)
Former Names: The club was formed by the
amalgamation of Wanderers FC and Excelsior FC
Nickname: 'Hatters'
Ground: Kenilworth Road Stadium, 1 Maple Road,
Luton   LU4 8AW
Ground Capacity: 10,226 (All seats)
Record Attendance: 30,069 (4th March 1959)

Pitch Size: 110 × 72 yards
Colours: Orange shirts with Blue shorts
Telephone N°: (01582) 411622
Ticket Office: (01582) 416976
Fax Number: (01582) 405070
Web Site: www.lutontown.co.uk
E-mail: info@lutontown.co.uk

GENERAL INFORMATION

Car Parking: Street parking
Coach Parking: Luton Bus Station
Nearest Railway Station: Luton (1 mile)
Nearest Bus Station: Bute Street, Luton
Club Shop: Kenilworth Road Forecourt and also at The Mall
in Luton town centre
Opening Times: 10.00am to 5.00pm
Telephone N°: (01582) 458368 (The Mall)

GROUND INFORMATION

Away Supporters' Entrances & Sections:
Oak Road for the Oak Stand

ADMISSION INFO (2017/2018 PRICES)

Adult Seating: £18.00 – £24.00
Under-10s Seating: £3.00 – £8.00
Under-17s Seating: £6.00 – £11.00
Under-22s Seating: £13.00 – £19.00
Senior Citizen Seating: £10.00 – £18.00
Note: Prices vary depending on the category of the game

FANS WITH DISABILITIES INFORMATION

Wheelchairs: 32 spaces in total for Home and Away fans in
the disabled section, Kenilworth Road End and Main Stand
Helpers: One helper admitted per disabled person
Prices: £18.00 – £23.00 for the disabled. Free for helpers
Disabled Toilets: Available adjacent to disabled area
Commentaries are available for the blind
Contact: (01582) 416976   (Bookings are necessary)

Travelling Supporters' Information:
Routes: From the North and West: Exit the M1 at Junction 11 and follow signs for Luton (A505) into Dunstable Road. Follow
the one-way system and turn right back towards Dunstable, take the second left into Ash Road for the ground; From the South
and East: Exit the M1 at Junction 10 (or A6/A612) into Luton Town Centre and follow signs into Dunstable Road. After the
railway bridge, take the sixth turning on the left into Ash Road for the ground.

MANCHESTER CITY FC

Founded: 1887 (**Entered League**: 1892)
Former Name: St.Mark's FC, Ardwick FC (1887-1894)
Nickname: 'Cityzens' 'City' 'Blues'
Ground: Etihad Stadium, Etihad Campus,
Manchester M11 3FF
Ground Capacity: 47,726 (All seats)
Record Attendance: 47,422 (vs Spurs – 2012)

Pitch Size: 115 × 75 yards
Colours: Sky Blue shirtswith White shorts
Telephone Nº: (0161) 444-1894
Ticket Office: (0161) 444-1894
Fax Number: (0161) 438-7999
Web Site: www.mancity.com
E-mail: mancity@mancity.com

GENERAL INFORMATION

Car Parking: 1,000 spaces available at the stadium. Another 7,000 spaces are available off site in the vicinity.
Coach Parking: Around 40 spaces available at the stadium
Nearest Railway Station: Ashburys (15 minutes walk) or Manchester Piccadilly (20 minutes walk)
Nearest Bus Station: 53, 54, 185, 186, 216, 217, 230, 231, 232, 233, 234, 235, 236, X36 and X37 services all stop at the stadium
Club Shop: At the stadium + Market Street, Manchester
Opening Times: Monday to Saturday 9.00am to 5.30pm, Sundays 11.00am to 5.00pm and before and after matches.
Market Street: Monday to Saturday 10.00am to 7.00pm, Sundays 11.00am to 5.00pm
Telephone Nº: (0161) 444-1894 Option 3

GROUND INFORMATION

Away Supporters' Entrances & Sections: South Stand

ADMISSION INFO (2017/2018 PRICES)

Please contact the club for details of ticket prices and availability for the 2017/2018 season.
Programme Price: £3.00

FANS WITH DISABILITIES INFORMATION

Wheelchairs: 197 spaces available in total
Helpers: One helper admitted per wheelchair
Prices: Please contact the club for details
Disabled Toilets: 30 toilets available around the stadium
Commentaries for the blind and lifts are also available
Contact: (0161) 444-1894 Option 1 (Bookings are recommended)

Travelling Supporters' Information:
Routes: From the North: Exit the M60 at Junction 23 onto the A635 then turn right onto the A662 Ashton New Road. The stadium is approximately 1½ miles on the right hand side; From the East: Exit the M60 at Junction 24 and follow the A57 into Manchester before turning right onto the A6010 for the stadium; From the South: Follow the A6 into Manchester and then turn right onto the A6010 for the stadium. Alternatively, exit the M60 at Junction 1 and follow the A34 Kingsway into Manchester before turning right onto the A6010 for the stadium; From the West: Take the M602 into Manchester and continue onto the A57 then the A57(M) Mancunian Way onto the A635. Follow the road right before turning left onto the A6010 for the stadium.

MANCHESTER UNITED FC

Founded: 1878 (**Entered League**: 1892)
Former Names: Newton Heath LYR FC (1878-1892),
Newton Heath FC (1892-1902)
Nickname: 'Red Devils'
Ground: Sir Matt Busby Way, Old Trafford,
Manchester   M16 0RA
Ground Capacity: 76,022 (All seats)
Record Attendance: 76,962 (25th March 1939)

Pitch Size: 115 × 76 yards
Colours: Red shirts with White shorts
Telephone Nº: (0161) 868-8000 Option 4
Ticket Information: (0161) 868-8000 Option 1
Fax Number: (0161) 868-8804
Web Site: www.manutd.com
E-mail: enquiries@manutd.co.uk

GENERAL INFORMATION

Car Parking: Lancashire Cricket Ground and Car Park E3 on John Gilbert Way. Other approved car parks are signposted
Coach Parking: By Police direction
Nearest Railway Station: At the ground
Nearest Bus Station: Chorlton Street
Nearest Metro Station: Old Trafford, located at L.C.C.C. and also Salford Quays
Club Shop: At the ground
Opening Times: Weekdays 9.00am – 5.30pm; Matchdays 9.00am to kick-off + 1 hour after match; Sundays 10.30am – 4.30pm; Non-match Saturdays 9.00am – 5.00pm
Telephone Nº: 0333 014-4543
Museum & Tour Centre: (0161) 868-8000 (Option 3)

GROUND INFORMATION

Away Supporters' Entrances & Sections:
South Stand (turnstile 22) & East Stand (turnstile 30)

ADMISSION INFO (2017/2018 PRICES)

Please contact the club for details of ticket prices and availability for the 2017/2018 season.
Programme Price: £3.00

FANS WITH DISABILITIES INFORMATION

Wheelchairs: 104 spaces in total for Home and Away fans in the a special section in front of 'L' Stand
Helpers: One helper admitted per fan with disabilities
Prices: Free of charge for fans with disabilities and helpers
Disabled Toilets: Available
Commentaries are available for the visually impaired
Contact: (0161) 868-8000 (Bookings are necessary)
E-mail: accessibility@manutd.co.uk

Travelling Supporters' Information:
Routes: From the North and West: Take the M61 to the M60 and exit at Junction 4 following Manchester (A5081) signs. Turn right after 2½ miles into Sir Matt Busby Way for the ground; From the South: Exit the M6 at Junction 19 and take Stockport (A556) road then Altrincham (A56). From Altrincham follow Manchester signs and turn left into Sir Matt Busby Way after 6 miles; From the East: Exit the M62 at Junction 17 and take the A56 to Manchester. Follow signs for the South then signs for Chester (Chester Road). Turn right into Sir Matt Busby Way after 2 miles.

MANSFIELD TOWN FC

Founded: 1897 (**Re-entered League**: 1892)
Former Name: Mansfield Wesleyans FC (1897-1905)
Nickname: 'Stags'
Ground: One Call Stadium, Quarry Lane, Mansfield, Nottinghamshire NG18 5DA
Ground Capacity: 10,000 (All seats)
Record Attendance: 24,467 (10th January 1953)
Pitch Size: 110 × 70 yards

Colours: Amber shirts with Royal Blue piping, Royal Blue shorts with Amber flash
Telephone Nº: (01623) 482482
Ticket Office: (01623) 482482
Fax Number: (01623) 482495
Web Site: www.mansfieldtown.net
E-mail: info@mansfieldtown.net

GENERAL INFORMATION

Car Parking: Large car park at the ground (£2.50)
Coach Parking: Adjacent to the ground
Nearest Railway Station: Mansfield (5 minutes walk)
Nearest Bus Station: Mansfield
Club Shop: In the South Stand of the Stadium
Opening Times: Weekdays 9.00am – 5.00pm and Matchdays 10.00am – 3.00pm
Telephone Nº: (01623) 482482

GROUND INFORMATION

Away Supporters' Entrances & Sections:
North Stand turnstiles for North Stand seating

ADMISSION INFO (2017/2018 PRICES)

Adult Seating: £22.00 – £24.00
Senior Citizen Seating: £18.00 – £20.00
Young Adult Seating: £17.00 – £19.00
Junior Seating: £14.00 – £16.00
Under-7s Seating: Free of charge
Note: There is a £2.00 discount for tickets bought in advance.

FANS WITH DISABILITIES INFORMATION

Wheelchairs: 90 spaces available in total in special sections in the North Stand, Quarry Street Stand and West Stand
Helpers: Admitted
Prices: Normal prices apply for the disabled. Free for helpers
Disabled Toilets: Available in the North Stand, West Stand and Quarry Lane Stand
Contact: (01623) 482482   (Please buy tickets in advance)

Travelling Supporters' Information:
Routes: From the North: Exit the M1 at Junction 29 and take the A617 to Mansfield. After 6¼ miles turn right at the Leisure Centre into Rosemary Street. Carry on to Quarry Lane and turn right; From the South and West: Exit the M1 at Junction 28 and take the A38 to Mansfield. After 6½ miles turn right at the crossroads into Belvedere Street then turn right after ¼ mile into Quarry Lane; From the East: Take the A617 to Rainworth, turn left at the crossroads after 3 miles into Windsor Road and turn right at the end into Nottingham Road, then left into Quarry Lane.

MIDDLESBROUGH FC

Founded: 1876 (**Entered League**: 1899)
Nickname: 'Boro'
Ground: Riverside Stadium, Middlesbrough, TS3 6RS
Ground Capacity: 34,712 (All seats)
Record Attendance: 34,836 (28th December 2004)
Pitch Size: 115 × 75 yards

Colours: Shirts are Red with a White sash, shorts are White
Telephone Nº: 0844 499-6789
Ticket Office: 0844 499-1234
Fax Number: (01642) 757697
Web Site: www.mfc.co.uk
E-mail: enquiries@mfc.co.uk

GENERAL INFORMATION

Car Parking: 1,250 spaces available
Coach Parking: At the ground
Nearest Railway Station: Middlesbrough (½ mile)
Nearest Bus Station: Middlesbrough
Club Shops: At ground
Opening Times: Weekdays 9.30am – 5.00pm and Saturday Matchdays 9.30am until kick-off
Telephone Nº: 0844 499-2676

GROUND INFORMATION

Away Supporters' Entrances & Sections:
South Stand turnstiles for the South Stand

ADMISSION INFO (2017/2018 PRICES)

Adult Seating: £27.00 – £34.00
Senior Citizen Seating: £18.00 – £26.00
Under-18s Seating: £13.00 – £17.00
Programme Price: £3.00

FANS WITH DISABILITIES INFORMATION

Wheelchairs: 170 spaces in total for home and away fans in the special areas in the West and South Stands
Helpers: One helper admitted per fan with disabilities
Prices: Please contact the club for further information
Disabled Toilets: Available in the West and South Stands
Contact: 0844 499-1234 (Bookings are necessary)
E-mail contact: supporters@mfc.co.uk

Travelling Supporters' Information:
Routes: From the North: Take the A19 across the flyover and join the A66 (Eastbound). At the end of the flyover, turn left at North Ormesby where the ground is well-signposted. The ground is 200 metres down the road; From the South: Take the A1 and A19 to the junction with the A66 (Eastbound). After the flyover, turn left at North Ormesby following signs for the ground.

MILLWALL FC

Founded: 1885 (**Entered League**: 1920)
Former Names: Millwall Rovers FC (1885-1893);
Millwall Athletic FC (1893-1925)
Nickname: 'The Lions'
Ground: The Den, Zampa Road, London SE16 3LN
Ground Capacity: 19,734 (All seats)
Record Attendance: 20,093 (10th January 1994)

Pitch Size: 116 × 74 yards
Colours: Dark Blue shirts with White shorts
Telephone Nº: (020) 7232-1222
Ticket Office: 0844 826-2004
Web Site: www.millwallfc.co.uk
E-mail: questions@millwallplc.com

GENERAL INFORMATION

Car Parking: Street parking
Coach Parking: Adjacent to the ground
Nearest Railway Station: New Cross Gate (1 mile) or
South Bermondsey (½ mile)
Nearest Tube: New Cross Gate (1 mile)/Canada Water (1 mile)
Club Shop: Next to the Stadium
Opening Times: Daily 9.30am to 4.30pm
Telephone Nº: (020) 7231-9845

GROUND INFORMATION

Away Supporters' Entrances & Sections:
North Stand turnstiles 31-36. A walkway from South
Bermondsey Station to the ground is open on matchdays

ADMISSION INFO (2017/2018 PRICES)

Adult Seating: £22.00 – £30.00
Under-16s Seating: £10.00 – £13.00
Under-12s Seating: £5.00 – £7.00
Concessionary Seating: £14.00 – £20.00
Note: Prices vary depending on the category of the game
Programme Price: £3.00

FANS WITH DISABILITIES INFORMATION

Wheelchairs: 78 spaces in the West Stand and 17 spaces
for away fans in front of the North Stand
Helpers: One helper admitted per wheelchair
Prices: Standard prices for fans with disabilities. Helpers free
Disabled Toilets: 17 toilets available around the Stadium
Commentaries are available for the blind
Contact: (020) 7232-1222 (Bookings are necessary)

Travelling Supporters' Information:
Routes: From the North: Follow City signs from the M1/A1 then signs for Shoreditch & Whitechapel. Follow Ring Road signs for Dover, cross over Tower Bridge and after 1 mile take 1st exit at the roundabout onto the A2. From Elephant and Castle take the A2 (New Kent Road) into Old Kent Road and turn left after 4 miles into Ilderton Road to Zampa Road; From the South: Take the A20 & A21 following signs to London. At New Cross follow signs for Surrey Quays into Kender Street, turn left into Old Kent Road then right into Ilderton Road. Zampa Road is the 7th turning on the right; From the East: Take the A2 to New Cross (then as from the South); From the West: From M4 & M3 follow the South Circular (A205) then follow signs for Clapham, the City (A3) then Camberwell to New Cross and then as from South.

NEWCASTLE UNITED FC

Founded: 1882 (**Entered League**: 1893)
Former Names: Newcastle East End FC (1882-1892)
amalgamated with Newcastle West End FC
Nickname: 'Magpies'
Ground: St. James Park, Newcastle-Upon-Tyne,
NE1 4ST
Ground Capacity: 52,354 (All seats)

Record Attendance: 68,386 (3rd September 1930)
Pitch Size: 115 × 74 yards
Colours: Black and White striped shirts, Black shorts
Telephone Nº: 0844 372-1892
Ticket Office: 0844 372-1892
Web Site: www.nufc.co.uk
E-mail: boxoffice@nufc.co.uk

GENERAL INFORMATION

Car Parking: Street parking
Coach Parking: By Police direction
Nearest Railway Station: Newcastle Central (¼ mile)
Nearest Bus Station: St. James' Boulevard (¼ mile)
Club Shop: At the ground
Opening Times: Monday to Saturday 9.00am – 5.00pm
Telephone Nº: 0844 372-1892

GROUND INFORMATION

Away Supporters' Entrances & Sections:
Rear of the Leazes Stand, entrance from Barrack Road

ADMISSION INFO (2017/2018 PRICES)

Adult Seating: £27.00 – £64.00
Child Seating: £14.00 – £34.00 (in the Family Seating Area)
Senior Citizen Seating: £22.00 – £52.00
Programme Price: £3.00

FANS WITH DISABILITIES INFORMATION

Wheelchairs: 160 spaces in total in special areas
throughout the stadium
Helpers: One helper admitted per fan with disabilities
Prices: Prices available on application
Disabled Toilets: Available throughout the stadium
Commentaries are available for 20 blind supporters
Contact: Please contact the Ticket Office for information

Travelling Supporters' Information:
Routes: From the North: Follow the A1 into Newcastle, then follow Hexham signs into Percy Street. Turn right into Leazes Park Road; From the South: Take the A1M, then after Birtley Granada Services take the A1 Gateshead Western Bypass (bear left on the Motorway). Follow Airport signs for approximately 3 miles then take the A692 (Newcastle) sign, crossing the Redheugh Bridge. Proceed over three sets of traffic lights to the roundabout and take the 1st exit into Barrack Road; From the West: Take the A69 towards the City Centre. Pass Newcastle General Hospital. At the traffic lights after the Hospital turn left into Brighton Grove. After 70 yards turn right into Stanhope Street and proceed into Barrack Road for the ground.

NEWPORT COUNTY AFC

Founded: 1989 (**Entered League**: 2013)
Former Names: Newport AFC
Nickname: 'The Exiles'
Ground: Rodney Parade, Newport NP19 0UU
Record Attendance: 4,616 (11th November 2006)
Pitch Size: 112 × 72 yards

Colours: Amber shirts with Black shorts
Telephone Nº: (01633) 481896
Ground Capacity: 7,850
Seating Capacity: 1,236
Web site: www.newport-county.co.uk
E-mail: office@newport-county.co.uk

GENERAL INFORMATION

Car Parking: Street parking only
Coach Parking: By Police direction
Nearest Railway Station: Newport (½ mile)
Nearest Bus Station: Newport
Club Shop: At the ground
Opening Times: Weekdays from 9.00am to 5.00pm.
Saturdays 9.00am to 1.00pm and for 30 minutes after the
final whistle on matchdays.
Telephone Nº: (01633) 481896

GROUND INFORMATION

Away Supporters' Entrances & Sections:
Sytner End turnstiles for Bisley Stand accommodation

ADMISSION INFO (2017/2018 PRICES)

Adult Standing: £18.00
Adult Seating: £20.00
Senior Citizen Standing/Seating: £16.00
Ages 16 to 21 Standing: £12.00
Ages 16 to 21 Seating: £14.00
Under-16s Standing/Seating: £8.00
Under-12s Standing/Seating: £6.00
Note: Under-6s are admitted free of charge

FANS WITH DISABILITIES INFORMATION

Wheelchairs: Accommodated
Helpers: Admitted
Prices: Normal prices for fans with disabilities. Helpers free
Disabled Toilets: Available
Contact: (01633) 481896 (Bookings are not necessary)

Travelling Supporters' Information:
Routes: From the West: Exit the M4 at Junction 26 of the M4 and take the 3rd exit at the roundabout onto Malpas Road. Take
the 2nd exit at the next roundabout then the 1st exit at the following roundabout across the River Usk bridge. * At the next set
of traffic lights bear right onto Chepstow Road, take the first right onto Cedar Road then the first right onto Corporation Road.
Take the next left onto Grafton Road and Rodney Parade is on left hand side; From The East: Exit the M4 at Junction 25A and
take the 1st exit at the roundabout onto Heidenheim Way. Take the 1st exit off the fly-over then the 2nd exit at the first roundabout then the 1st exit at the next roundabout across the River Usk bridge. Then as above *.

NORTHAMPTON TOWN FC

Founded: 1897 (**Entered League**: 1920)
Nickname: 'Cobblers'
Ground: Sixfields Stadium, Upton Way,
Northampton   NN5 5QA
Ground Capacity: Approximately 8,000 (All seats)
Record Attendance: 7,557 (26th September 1998)
Pitch Size: 116 × 72 yards

Colours: Claret and White shirts with White shorts
Telephone Nº: (01604) 683700
Ticket Office: (01604) 683777
Fax Number: (01604) 751613
Web Site: www.ntfc.co.uk

GENERAL INFORMATION
Car Parking: At the ground
Coach Parking: At the ground
Nearest Railway Station: Northampton Castle (2 miles)
Nearest Bus Station: North Gate
Club Shop: At the ground
Opening Times: Monday to Thursday 10.00am – 5.00pm,
Friday 10.00am – 5.00pm, non-match Saturdays 10.00am –
12.00pm and Matchdays 10.00am to kick-off and 30 minutes
after the final whistle
Telephone Nº: (01604) 683777

GROUND INFORMATION
Away Supporters' Entrances & Sections:
South Stand

ADMISSION INFO (2017/2018 PRICES)
Adult Seating: £24.00
Senior Citizen Seating: £20.00
Under-21s Seating: £18.00
Under-18s Seating: £12.00
Under-7s: Admitted free of charge
Note: Discounted prices are available for advance purchases

FANS WITH DISABILITIES INFORMATION
Wheelchairs: 80 spaces in total for Home and Away fans in
various areas of the ground
Helpers: One helper admitted per fan with disabilities
Prices: £16.00 for fans with disabilities. Helpers free
Disabled Toilets: Available
Commentaries are available for the blind
Contact: (01604) 683777   (Bookings are necessary)

Travelling Supporters' Information:
Routes: From All Parts: Exit the M1 at Junction 15A following the signs for Sixfields Leisure onto Upton Way – the ground is
approximately 2 miles.

NORWICH CITY FC

Founded: 1902 (**Entered League**: 1920)
Nickname: 'Canaries'
Ground: Carrow Road, Norwich NR1 1JE
Ground Capacity: 27,244 (All seats)
Record Attendance: 43,984 (30th March 1963)
Pitch Size: 114 × 74 yards

Colours: Yellow shirts with Green shorts
Telephone Nº: (01603) 760760
Ticket Office: 0844 826-1902
Fax Number: (01603) 613886
Web Site: www.canaries.co.uk
E-mail: reception@ncfc-canaries.co.uk

GENERAL INFORMATION
Car Parking: City Centre car parks (nearby)
Coach Parking: Lower Clarence Road
Nearest Railway Station: Norwich Thorpe (1 mile)
Nearest Bus Station: Surrey Street, Norwich
Club Shop: At the ground and also stores in Chapelfield and the Castle Mall
Opening Times: Carrow Road store opens Monday to Saturday 9.00am to 5.30pm and Sunday 10.00am to 4.00pm
Telephone Nº: 0844 826-1902

GROUND INFORMATION
Away Supporters' Entrances & Sections:
Jarrold Stand usings turnstiles 51-57

ADMISSION INFO (2017/2018 PRICES)
Adult Seating: £18.00 – £50.00
Senior Citizen Seating: £8.00 – £30.00
Under-18s Seating: £3.00 – £25.00
Under-12s Seating: £1.00 – £17.00
Note: Discounted prices are available for advance purchases and to club members.

FANS WITH DISABILITIES INFORMATION
Wheelchairs: 74 spaces for home fans and 15 for away fans in Jarrold/Aviva Community Stand. Plenty of spaces are also available for ambulant fans with disabilities
Helpers: One helper admitted per fan with disabilities
Prices: A single price is charged for each fan with disabilities and a helper. Please contact the club for further details
Disabled Toilets: Available
Contact: 0844 826-1902 (Bookings are necessary)

Travelling Supporters' Information:
Routes: From the South: Take the A11 or A140 and turn right onto the A47 towards Great Yarmouth & Lowestoft, take the A146 Norwich/Lowestoft sliproad, turn left towards Norwich and follow road signs for the Football Ground; From the West: Take the A47 on to the A146 Norwich/Lowestoft slip road. Turn left towards Norwich, follow the road signs for the Football Ground.

NOTTINGHAM FOREST FC

Founded: 1865 (**Entered League**: 1892)	**Colours**: Red shirts with White shorts
Nickname: 'The Reds'	**Telephone Nº**: (0115) 982-4444
Ground: The City Ground, Nottingham NG2 5FJ	**Ticket Office**: (0115) 982-4388
Ground Capacity: 30,445 (All seats)	**Fax Number**: (0115) 982-4455
Record Attendance: 49,946 (28th October 1967)	**Web Site**: www.nottinghamforest.co.uk
Pitch Size: 112 × 76 yards	**E-mail**: enquiries@nottinghamforest.co.uk

GENERAL INFORMATION

Car Parking: Various nearby car parks and street parking
Coach Parking: Available at the stadium.
Nearest Railway Station: Nottingham Midland (½ mile)
Nearest Bus Station: Victoria Street/Broadmarsh Centre
Club Shop: At the ground
Opening Times: Weekdays 9.00am – 5.00pm; Matchdays 9.00am – kick-off and 30 minutes after the game; Sunday matchdays 10.00am – kick-off + 30 minutes after the game
Telephone Nº: (0115) 982-4460

GROUND INFORMATION

Away Supporters' Entrances & Sections:
Entrances via East car park for Bridgford Stand

ADMISSION INFO (2017/2018 PRICES)

Due to the introduction of a 'dynamic' pricing system, we suggest that fans contact the club for further details about admission prices for any particular game.
Programme Price: £3.00

FANS WITH DISABILITIES INFORMATION

Wheelchairs: 68 spaces in total for home fans around the ground plus 11 spaces for away fans in the Lower Bridgford Stand
Helpers: One helper admitted per fan with disabilities
Prices: Please contact the club for further information
Disabled Toilets: 7 available with radar key locks
Contact: (0115) 982-4341 (Bookings are necessary)

Travelling Supporters' Information:
Routes: From the North: Exit the M1 at Junction 26 following Nottingham signs (A610) then signs to Melton Mowbray and Trent Bridge (A606). Cross the River Trent, turn left into Radcliffe Road then left again into Colwick Road for the ground; From the South: Exit the M1 at Junction 24 following signs for Nottingham (South) to Trent Bridge. Turn right into Radcliffe Road then left into Colwick Road; From the East: Take the A52 to West Bridgford and follow signs for Football & Cricket; From the West: Take the A52 into Nottingham, follow signs for Melton Mowbray and Trent Bridge, cross the River Trent (then as North).

NOTTS COUNTY FC

Founded: 1862 (**Entered League**: 1888)
Nickname: 'The Magpies'
Ground: Meadow Lane, Nottingham   NG2 3HJ
Ground Capacity: 20,300 (All seats)
Record Attendance: 47,310 (12th March 1955)
Pitch Size: 113 × 70 yards

Colours: Black and White striped shirts, Black shorts
Telephone N°: (0115) 952-9000
Ticket Office: (0115) 955-7210
Fax Number: (0115) 955-3994
Web Site: www.nottscountyfc.co.uk
E-mail: office@nottscountyfc.co.uk

GENERAL INFORMATION
Car Parking: British Waterways, Meadow Lane
Coach Parking: Incinerator Road (Cattle Market Corner)
Nearest Railway Station: Nottingham Midland (½ mile)
Nearest Bus Station: Broadmarsh Centre
Club Shop: At the ground
Opening Times: Mondays to Friday 9.00am – 5.00pm,
Saturday Matchdays 9.00am – 5.30pm, other Saturdays
9.00am – 1.00pm
Telephone N°: (0115) 955-7205

GROUND INFORMATION
Away Supporters' Entrances & Sections:
Jimmy Sirrel Stand, Block Z – use Turnstiles 19-24

ADMISSION INFO (2017/2018 PRICES)
Adult Seating: £22.00
Under-18s Seating: £9.00
Ages 18 to 21 Seating: £16.00
Senior Citizen Seating: £16.00
Under-16s Seating: £7.00
Under-12s Seating: £1.00 (Under-7s admitted free)
Note: Discounted prices are available for advance purchases
Programme Price: £3.00

FANS WITH DISABILITIES INFORMATION
Wheelchairs: 34 spaces for home fans in the Derek Pavis
Stand and Haydn Green Family Stand and 10 spaces for away
fans in the Jimmy Sirrel Stand
Helpers: One helper admitted per fan with disabilities
Prices: Normal prices apply for fans with disabilities.
Disabled Toilets: Available
Contact: (0115) 955-7204 (Bookings are necessary)

Travelling Supporters' Information:
Routes: From the North: Exit the M1 at Junction 26 following Nottingham signs (A610) then Melton Mowbray and Trent
Bridge (A606) signs. Before the River Trent turn left into Meadow Lane; From the South: Exit the M1 at Junction 24 following
signs for Nottingham (South) to Trent Bridge, cross the river and follow the one-way system to the right, then turn left and right
at the traffic lights then second right into Meadow Lane; From the East: Take the A52 to West Bridgford/Trent Bridge, cross the
river and follow the one-way system to the right then turn left and right at the traffic lights, then second right into Meadow
Lane; From the West: Take the A52 into Nottingham following signs for Melton Mowbray and Trent Bridge. Before the River
Trent turn left into Meadow Lane.

OLDHAM ATHLETIC FC

Founded: 1895 (**Entered League**: 1907)
Former Names: Pine Villa FC (1895-1899)
Nickname: 'Latics'
Ground: Boundary Park, Furtherwood Road,
Oldham   OL1 2PA
Ground Capacity: 13,612 (All seats)
Record Attendance: 47,671 (25th January 1930)

Pitch Size: 110 × 72 yards
Colours: Blue shirts, shorts and socks
Telephone Nº: (0161) 624-4972
Ticket Office: (0161) 785-5150
Fax Number: (0161) 627-5915
Web Site: www.oldhamathletic.co.uk
E-mail: enquiries@oldhamathletic.co.uk

GENERAL INFORMATION

Car Parking: North Stand car park (350 cars)
Coach Parking: At the ground
Nearest Railway Station: Oldham Werneth (1½ miles)
Nearest Bus Station: Oldham Town Centre (2 miles)
Club Shop: In the North Stand
Opening Times: Daily from 9.00am to 6.00pm.
Telephone Nº: (0161) 785-5169

GROUND INFORMATION

Away Supporters' Entrances & Sections:
Chadderton Road Stand

ADMISSION INFO (2016/2017 PRICES)

Adult Seating: £20.00 – £24.00
Concessionary Seating: £12.00
Under-16s Seating: £10.00
Under-12s Seating: £5.00
Programme Price: £3.00

FANS WITH DISABILITIES INFORMATION

Wheelchairs: 60 spaces in the special areas in the North
Stand, Chadderton Road Stand and Rochdale Road Stand
Helpers: One helper admitted per fan with disabilities
Prices: Normal prices for fans with disabilities. Helpers free
Disabled Toilets: Available in the North Stand, Rochdale
Road Stand and the Chadderton Road Stand
Contact: (0161) 785-5179   (Bookings are necessary)

Travelling Supporters' Information:
Routes: From All Parts: Exit the M62 at Junction 20 and take the A627M to the junction with the A664. Take the 1st exit at the
roundabout onto Broadway, then the 1st right into Hilbre Avenue which leads to the car park at the ground.

OXFORD UNITED FC

Founded: 1893 (**Re-Entered League**: 2010)
Former Names: Headington United FC (1893-1960)
Nickname: 'U's'
Ground: Kassam Stadium, Grenoble Road, Oxford, OX4 4XP
Ground Capacity: 12,205 (All seats)
Record Attendance: 22,730 (At the Manor Ground)

Pitch Size: 110 × 70 yards
Colours: Yellow shirts with Navy Blue shorts
Telephone Nº: (01865) 337500
Ticket Office: (01865) 337533
Fax Number: (01865) 337501
Web Site: www.oufc.co.uk
E-mail: admin@oufc.co.uk

GENERAL INFORMATION

Car Parking: 2,000 free spaces available at the ground
Coach Parking: At the ground
Nearest Railway Station: Oxford (4 miles)
Nearest Bus Station: Oxford
Club Shop: At the ground
Opening Times: Monday to Friday 10.00am – 5.00pm and Matchdays from 10.00am until kick-off
Telephone Nº: (01865) 747231

GROUND INFORMATION

Away Supporters' Entrances & Sections:
North Stand turnstiles for North Stand accommodation. Ticket office for away supporters is adjacent

ADMISSION INFO (2017/2018 PRICES)

Adult Seating: £20.00 – £28.00
Under-21s Seating: £14.00 – £20.00
Under-18s Seating: £12.00 – £20.00
Under-7s Seating: Free with a paying adult in the Family Area. Otherwise £5.00 – £12.00
Senior Citizen Seating: £14.00 – £21.00
Programme Price: £3.00

FANS WITH DISABILITIES INFORMATION

Wheelchairs: Accommodated in areas in the North, East and South Stands
Helpers: One assistant admitted per fan with disabilities
Prices: Normal prices for fans with disabilities. One assistant also admitted free of charge if required
Disabled Toilets: Available throughout the ground
Contact: (01865) 337533   (Bookings are not necessary)

Travelling Supporters' Information:
Routes: From the Oxford Ring Road take the A4074 towards Henley and Reading then turn left after ½ mile following signs for the Oxford Science Park. Bear left and go straight on at two roundabouts then the Stadium is on the left in Grenoble Road. The Kassam Stadium is clearly signposted on all major roads in Oxford.

PETERBOROUGH UNITED FC

Founded: 1934 (**Entered League**: 1960)
Nickname: 'Posh'
Ground: The Abax Stadium, London Road, Peterborough   PE2 8AL
Ground Capacity: 15,314
Seating Capacity: 10,000
Record Attendance: 30,096 (20th February 1965)
Pitch Size: 112 × 71 yards

Colours: Cobalt Blue shirts with Blue shorts
Telephone Nº: (01733) 563947
Ticket Office: 0844 847-1934
Fax Number: (01733) 344140
Web Site: www.theposh.com
E-mail: info@theposh.com

GENERAL INFORMATION

Car Parking: At the ground and also adjacent
Coach Parking: In front of the (North) Main Stand
Nearest Railway Station: Peterborough (1 mile)
Nearest Bus Station: Peterborough (1 mile)
Club Shop: At the ground
Opening Times: Monday to Thursday 9.00am to 5.00pm, Fridays 10.00am to 5.00pm and Saturday Matchdays 10.00pm to 3.00pm then 5.00pm to 5.30pm
Telephone Nº: (01733) 865668

GROUND INFORMATION

Away Supporters' Entrances & Sections:
'A' North Block (Seating) only while the Moyes End Terrace undergoes redevelopment.

ADMISSION INFO (2017/2018 PRICES)

Adult Standing: £22.00 – £24.00
Adult Seating: £26.00 – £28.00
Senior Citizen Standing: £17.00 – £19.00
Senior Citizen Seating: £21.00 – £23.00
Under-22s Standing: £13.00 – £15.00
Under-22s Seating: £17.00 – £19.00
Under-12s Standing/Seating: £7.00 – £9.00
Under-7s Seating: £1.00
Note: Prices vary depending on the category of the game. Discounts are available for tickets purchased in advance
Programme Price: £3.00

FANS WITH DISABILITIES INFORMATION

Wheelchairs: 29 spaces available in total
Helpers: One helper admitted per fan with disabilities
Prices: Normal prices for fans with disabilities. Helpers free
Disabled Toilets: Available in the South and Main Stands
Contact: (01733) 865674 Option 2 (Bookings are necessary)

Travelling Supporters' Information:
Routes: From the North and West: Take the A1 then the A47 into the Town Centre and follow Whittlesey signs across the river into London Road; From the East: Take the A47 into the Town Centre (then as from the North); From the South: Take the A1 then the A15 into London Road.

PLYMOUTH ARGYLE FC

Founded: 1886 (**Entered League**: 1920)
Former Names: Argyle FC (1886-1903)
Nickname: 'Pilgrims' 'Argyle'
Ground: Home Park, Plymouth PL2 3DQ
Ground Capacity: 16,388 (All seats)
Record Attendance: 43,596 (10th October 1936)
Pitch Size: 112 × 72 yards

Colours: Green shirts and White shorts
Telephone Nº: (01752) 302207
Ticket Office: (01752) 907700
Web Site: www.pafc.co.uk
E-mail: argyle@pafc.co.uk

GENERAL INFORMATION

Car Parking: Car park for 1,000 cars is adjacent
Coach Parking: Central Park Car Park
Nearest Railway Station: Plymouth North Road
Nearest Bus Station: Coach hub off Mayflower Street
Club Shop: At the ground
Opening Times: Monday to Friday 9.00am to 5.00pm, Saturday home matchdays 9.00am to 3.00pm plus 30 minutes after the game. Saturday away matchdays 10.00am to 1.00pm.
Telephone Nº: (01752) 562561

GROUND INFORMATION

Away Supporters' Entrances & Sections:
Barn Park End turnstiles for covered accommodation

ADMISSION INFO (2017/2018 PRICES)

Adult Seating: £23.00
Under-18s Seating: £10.00
Senior Citizen Seating: £18.00
Note: Tickets are cheaper if purchased before the matchday.
Programme Price: £3.00

FANS WITH DISABILITIES INFORMATION

Wheelchairs: 60 spaces Home fans and 25 spaces for Away fans in special sections
Helpers: One helper admitted per fan with disabilities
Prices: £18.00 for fans with disabilities. Free for helpers
Disabled Toilets: Available throughout the stadium
Commentaries are available for the visually impaired
Contact: (01752) 562561   (Steph Barker – Bookings are necessary)

Travelling Supporters' Information:
Routes: From All Parts: Take the A38 to Tavistock Road (A386), then branch left following signs for Home Park (A386) and continue for 1¼ miles. The car park for the ground is on the left (signposted Home Park).

PORTSMOUTH FC

Founded: 1898 (**Entered League**: 1920)
Nickname: 'Pompey'
Ground: Fratton Park, 57 Frogmore Road,
Portsmouth, Hants   PO4 8RA
Ground Capacity: 18,931 (All seats)
Record Attendance: 51,385 (26th February 1949)
Pitch Size: 110 × 71 yards

Colours: Blue shirts with White shorts
Telephone Nº: (023) 9273-1204
Ticket Office: 0345 646-1898
Fax Number: (023) 9273-4129
Web Site: www.portsmouthfc.co.uk
E-mail: info@pompeyfc.co.uk

GENERAL INFORMATION

Car Parking: Street parking plus a limited number of spaces at Fratton Park (first come, first served – £10.00 charge)
Coach Parking: By Police direction
Nearest Railway Station: Fratton (adjacent)
Nearest Bus Station: The Hard, Portsmouth
Club Shop: Fratton Way
Opening Times: Monday to Friday 9.00am – 5.00pm (until 11.00pm on evening matchdays), Saturday 9.00am–6.00pm and Sunday 10.30am to 4.30pm.

GROUND INFORMATION

Away Supporters' Entrances & Sections:
Apsley Road – Milton Road side for Apsley Road End

ADMISSION INFO (2017/2018 PRICES)

Adult Seating: £25.00
Junior Seating: £10.00 (£5.00 when accompanied)
Senior Citizen Seating: £19.00 (Ages 63+)
Ages 17 to 22 Seating: £15.00
Note: Adults, Senior Citizens or Ages 17 to 22 must be accompanied by a Junior if they sit in the Family Section.
Programme Price: £3.00

FANS WITH DISABILITIES INFORMATION

Wheelchairs: Limited number of spaces available in a special section in the Fratton End
Helpers: One helper admitted per fan with disabilities
Prices: Please contact the club for pricing information. Free of charge for helpers
Disabled Toilets: One available in disabled section
Contact: (023) 9273-1204 (Bookings are necessary)

Travelling Supporters' Information:
Routes: From the North and West: Take the M27 and M275 to the end then take the 2nd exit at the roundabout and after ¼ mile turn right at the 'T' junction into London Road (A2047). After 1¼ miles cross the railway bridge and turn left into Goldsmith Avenue. After ½ mile turn left into Frogmore Road; From the East: Take the A27 following Southsea signs (A2030). Turn left at the roundabout (3 miles) onto the A288, then right into Priory Crescent and next right into Carisbrooke Road for the ground.

PORT VALE FC

Founded: 1876 (**Entered League**: 1892)
Former Names: Burslem Port Vale FC
Nickname: 'Valiants'
Ground: Vale Park, Hamil Road, Burslem,
Stoke-on-Trent ST6 1AW
Ground Capacity: 19,148 (All seats)
Record Attendance: 49,768 (20nd February 1960)
Pitch Size: 114 × 77 yards

Colours: Shirts are white with Black pin stripes and
Amber trim, Shorts are White with Amber trim
Telephone Nº: (01782) 655800
Ticket Office: (01782) 655816
Fax Number: (01782) 834981
Web Site: www.port-vale.co.uk
E-mail: enquiries@port-vale.co.uk

GENERAL INFORMATION

Car Parking: Car parks at the ground
Coach Parking: Hamil Road car park
Nearest Railway Station: Stoke
Nearest Bus Station: Burslem (adjacent)
Club Shop: At the ground
Opening Times: Monday to Saturday 9.00am – 5.00pm
Telephone Nº: (01782) 655826

GROUND INFORMATION

Away Supporters' Entrances & Sections:
Hamil Road turnstiles, numbers 1 to 8

ADMISSION INFO (2017/2018 PRICES)

Adult Seating: £22.00 – £23.00
Ages 9 to 17 Seating: £10.00
Ages 18 to 21 Seating: £17.00 – £18.00
Under-9s Seating: Free of charge
Concessionary Seating: £17.00 – £18.00
Programme Price: £3.00

FANS WITH DISABILITIES INFORMATION

Wheelchairs: 46 spaces available in a special area in the
Lorne Street/Bycars Corner
Helpers: One helper admitted per fan with disabilities
Prices: Normal prices for fans with disabilities. Helpers free
Disabled Toilets: Available
Commentaries are available – please contact the club
Contact: (01782) 655821   (Bookings are necessary)

Travelling Supporters' Information:
Routes: From the North: Exit the M6 at Junction 16 and follow Stoke signs (A500). Branch left off the A500 at the exit signposted
Tunstall and take the 2nd exit at the roundabout into Newcastle Street. Proceed through the traffic lights into Moorland Road
and take the 2nd turning on the left into Hamil Road; From the South and West: Exit the M6 at Junction 15 and take the A5006
and A500. After 6¼ miles branch left (then as from the North); From the East: Take the A50 or A52 into Stoke following Burslem
signs into Waterloo Road, turn right at Burslem crossroads into Moorland Road (then as from the North).

PRESTON NORTH END FC

Founded: 1880 (**Entered League**: 1888)
Nickname: 'Lilywhites' 'North End'
Ground: Deepdale, Preston   PR1 6RU
Ground Capacity: 23,404 (All seats)
Record Attendance: 42,684 (23rd April 1938)
Pitch Size: 109 × 73 yards   (100 × 67 metres)

Colours: White shirts with Blue shorts
Telephone Nº: 0344 856-1964
Ticket Office: 0344 856-1966
Web Site: www.pne.com
E-mail: enquiries@pne.com

GENERAL INFORMATION

Car Parking: Four official car parks at the stadium plus further parking at Moor Park School
Coach Parking: By prior arrangement with the club
Nearest Railway Station: Preston (2 miles)
Nearest Bus Station: Preston (1 mile)
Club Shop: At the ground
Opening Times: Monday to Saturday 9.00am to 5.00pm and midweek matchdays 9.00am until kick-off
Telephone Nº: 0344 856-1965

GROUND INFORMATION

Away Supporters' Entrances & Sections:
Bill Shankly Kop

ADMISSION INFO (2017/2018 PRICES)

Adult Seating: £24.00 – £30.00
Age 19 to 21/Student/Apprentice Seating: £16.00 – £23.00
Ages 12 to 18 Seating: £6.00 – £9.00
Under-12s Seating: £2.00
Senior Citizen Seating: £16.00 – £23.00
Programme Price: £3.00

FANS WITH DISABILITIES INFORMATION

Wheelchairs: Spaces are available for advance order
Helpers: One helper admitted per fan with disabilities
Prices: £24.00 – £30.00 for fans with disabilities. Helpers free
Disabled Toilets: Available throughout the ground
Commentaries are available for the blind
Contact: 0344 856-1966 (Bookings are usually necessary)

Travelling Supporters' Information:
Routes: From the North: Take the M6 then the M55 to Junction 1. Follow signs for Preston (A6). After 2 miles turn left at the crossroads into Blackpool Road (A5085). Turn right ¾ mile into Deepdale; From the South and East: Exit the M6 at Junction 31 and follow Preston signs (A59). Take the 2nd exit at the roundabout (1 mile) into Blackpool Road. Turn left after 1¼ miles into Deepdale; From the West: Exit the M55 at Junction 1 (then as from the North).

QUEEN'S PARK RANGERS FC

Founded: 1882 (**Entered League**: 1920)
Former Names: Formed by the amalgamation of
St. Jude's FC and Christchurch Rangers FC
Nickname: 'Rangers' 'R's'
Ground: Loftus Road Stadium, South Africa Road,
London   W12 7PJ
Ground Capacity: 18,136 (All seats)

Record Attendance: 35,353 (27th April 1974)
Pitch Size: 109 × 72 yards
Colours: Blue and White hooped shirts, White shorts
Telephone Nº: (020) 8743-0262
Ticket Office: 08444 777007
Fax Number: (020) 8749-0994
Web Site: www.qpr.co.uk

GENERAL INFORMATION

Car Parking: Street parking
Coach Parking: By Police direction
Nearest Railway Station: Shepherd's Bush
Nearest Tube Station: White City (Central) or Wood Lane
(Hammersmith & City)
Club Shop: Superstore at the ground
Opening Times: Weekdays 9.00am to 5.00pm. Non-match
Saturdays 9.00am to 5.00pm. Saturday matchdays 9.00am
until 15 minutes before kick-off then 45 minutes after game
(but not for evening matches)
Telephone Nº: (020) 8749-6862

GROUND INFORMATION

Away Supporters' Entrances & Sections:
Access via South Africa Road turnstile 2 for School End Lower
and Ellerslie Road turnstile 13 for School End Upper

ADMISSION INFO (2017/2018 PRICES)

Adult Seating: £30.00 – £39.00
Senior Citizen/Ages 18 to 21 Seating: £21.00 – £29.00
Under-18s Seating: £18.00 – £22.00
Note: Prices shown are for matchday ticket purchases.
Discounts are available to members and for advance purchases
Programme Price: £3.00

FANS WITH DISABILITIES INFORMATION

Wheelchairs: 24 spaces available
Helpers: One helper admitted per wheelchair
Prices: Concessionary prices for fans with disabilities.
Free of charge for helpers
Disabled Toilets: Available
Commentaries for the blind are available in the Ellerslie Road
Stand. Please contact the Ticket Office to arrange this facility.
Contact: (020) 8740-2502   (Bookings are necessary)

Travelling Supporters' Information:
Routes: From the North: Take M1 & M406 North Circular for Neasden, go left after ¾ mile (A404) following signs for Harlesden,
Hammersmith, past White City Stadium, right into White City Road and left into South Africa Road; From the South: Take A206
then A3 across Putney Bridge and follow signs to Hammersmith then Oxford (A219) to Shepherd's Bush. Join the A4020 following
signs to Acton, turn right (¼ mile) into Loftus Road; From the East: Take the A12, A406 then the A503 to join the Ring Road,
follow Oxford signs and join the A40(M), branch left (2 miles) to the M41, take the 3rd exit at the roundabout to the A4020 (then
as South); From the West: Take the M4 to Chiswick then the A315 & A402 to Shepherd's Bush, join A4020 (then as South).

READING FC

Founded: 1871 (**Entered League**: 1920)
Former Names: Formed by the amalgamation of
Hornets FC (1877) and Earley FC (1889)
Nickname: 'Royals'
Ground: Madejski Stadium, Junction 11 M4,
Reading, Berkshire   RG2 0FL
Ground Capacity: 24,200 (All seats)
Record Attendance: 24,184 (17th November 2012)

Pitch Size: 114 × 74 yards
Colours: Blue and White hooped shirts, White shorts
Telephone Nº: (0118) 968-1100
Ticket Office: (0118) 968-1313
Fax Number: (0118) 968-1101
Web Site: www.readingfc.co.uk
E-mail: customerservice@readingfc.co.uk

GENERAL INFORMATION

Car Parking: 1,800 spaces available at the ground. Also
another 2,000 spaces available nearby
Coach Parking: Please contact the club for details
Nearest Railway Station: Reading Central
Nearest Bus Station: Reading
Club Shop: At the ground
Opening Times: Monday to Saturday 9.00am – 5.30pm,
Sundays 10.00am – 4.00pm
Telephone Nº: (0118) 968-1234

GROUND INFORMATION

Away Supporters' Entrances & Sections:
South Stand entrances and accommodation

ADMISSION INFO (2017/2018 PRICES)

Adult Seating: £25.00 – £35.00
Over-65s Seating: £16.00 – £25.00
Ages 18 to 24 Seating: £13.00 – £20.00
Under-17s Seating: £8.00 – £17.00
Note: Prices shown are for matchday ticket purchases.
Discounts are available to members and for advance purchases
Programme Price: £3.00

FANS WITH DISABILITIES INFORMATION

Wheelchairs: A total of 128 spaces are available for
wheelchairs throughout the stadium
Helpers: Yes
Prices: Normal prices apply for fans with disabilities. Free of
charge for helpers.
Disabled Toilets: Available
Commentaries for approximately 12 people are available
Contact: (0118) 968-1208   (Bookings are necessary)
E-mail: disability@readingfc.co.uk

Travelling Supporters' Information:
Routes: The stadium is situated just off Junction 11 of the M4 near Reading.

ROCHDALE FC

Founded: 1907 (**Entered League**: 1921)
Former Names: Rochdale Town FC
Nickname: 'The Dale'
Ground: Spotland Stadium, Rochdale OL11 5DS
Ground Capacity: 10,003
Seating Capacity: 7,913
Record Attendance: 24,231 (10th December 1949)

Pitch Size: 114 × 76 yards
Colours: Blue shirts and shorts
Telephone Nº: 0844 826-1907
Ticket Office: 0844 826-1907 Option 8
Fax Number: (01706) 648466
Web Site: www.rochdaleafc.co.uk
E-mail: office@rochdaleafc.co.uk

GENERAL INFORMATION

Car Parking: Street parking only
Coach Parking: By Police direction
Nearest Railway Station: Rochdale (2 miles)
Nearest Bus Station: Town Centre (1 mile)
Club Shop: At the ground
Opening Times: Weekdays and Saturday Matchdays from 9.00am to 5.00pm
Telephone Nº: 0844 826-1907 Option 3

GROUND INFORMATION

Away Supporters' Entrances & Sections:
Turnstiles 11 to 18 for Willbutts Lane

ADMISSION INFO (2017/2018 PRICES)

Adult Standing: £17.00
Adult Seating: £20.00 – £22.00
Ages 16 to 21/Senior Citizen Standing: £12.00
Ages 16 to 21/Senior Citizen Seating: £14.00 – £16.00
Under-16s Standing/Seating: £5.00
Programme Price: £3.00

FANS WITH DISABILITIES INFORMATION

Wheelchairs: 24 spaces in total in special sections in the Main, Pearl Street and Willbutts Lane Stands
Helpers: One helper admitted per fan with disabilities
Prices: £16.00 for fans with disabilities. Free for helpers
Disabled Toilets: Available
Contact: (01706) 644648 (Bookings are necessary)

Travelling Supporters' Information:
Routes: From All Parts: Exit the M62 at Junction 20 and take the A627(M) signposted Rochdale. At the end of this link road, filter left carry on for 400 yards and go straight on at the roundabout into Roche Valley Way signposted Spotland Stadium. At the traffic lights go staight ahead and the ground is on the right after ½ mile.

ROTHERHAM UNITED FC

Founded: 1870 (**Entered League**: 1893)
Former Names: Rotherham Town FC (1870-1896), Thornhill United FC (1884-1905) and Rotherham County FC (1905-1925)
Nickname: 'The Millers'
Ground: AESSEAL New York Stadium, New York Way, Rotherham   S60 1AH
Ground Capacity: 12,000 (All seats)
Pitch Size: 110 × 72 yards

Record Attendance: 11,758 (7th September 2013)
Colours: Red shirts with White sleeves, White shorts
Contact Telephone Nº: 08444 140733
Ticket Office: 08444 140754
Fax Number: 08444 140744
Web Site: www.themillers.co.uk
E-mail: office@rotherhamunited.net

GENERAL INFORMATION
Car Parking: Street Parking and in Sheffield Road car parks
Coach Parking: By police direction
Nearest Railway Station: Rotherham Central (½ mile)
Nearest Bus Station: Rotherham Town Centre (½ mile)
Club Shop: At the ground
Opening Times: Weekdays 9.00am to 5.00pm, Saturdays 9.00am to 1.00pm (until 3.00pm on Saturday Matchdays)
Telephone Nº: 08444 140754

GROUND INFORMATION
Away Supporters' Entrances & Sections:
Mears Stand

ADMISSION INFO (2016/2017 PRICES)
Adult Seating: £25.00 – £27.00
Senior Citizen/Student Seating: £15.00 – £17.00
Ages 13 to 17 Seating: £9.00 – £10.00
Ages 8 to 12 Seating: £7.00 – £8.00
Under-8s Seating: £2.00 in the Family Stand
Programme Price: £3.00

FANS WITH DISABILITIES INFORMATION
Wheelchairs: Accommodated
Helpers: One helper admitted with each fan with disabilities
Prices: Supporters with disabilities are charged concessionary prices. Helpers are admitted free of charge
Disabled Toilets: Available
Contact: 08444 140733   (Bookings are necessary)

Travelling Supporters' Information:
Routes: From the North: Exit the M1 at Junction 34, follow Rotherham (A6109) signs to the traffic lights and turn right. The ground is ¼ mile on the right; From the South & West: Exit the M1 at Junction 33, turn right and follow signs for Rotherham. Turn left at the roundabout then right at the next roundabout. Follow the dual carriageway and continue straight on at the next roundabout. Turn left at the followingroundabout and the ground is on the left after ¼ mile; From the East: Take the A630 into Rotherham following Sheffield signs. Turn left at the 3rd roundabout (signposted Masborough) and the ground is on the right.

SCUNTHORPE UNITED FC

Founded: 1899 (**Entered League**: 1950)
Former Name: Scunthorpe and Lindsey United FC (1899-1912)
Nickname: 'The Iron'
Ground: Glanford Park, Jack Brownsword Way, Scunthorpe, North Lincolnshire   DN15 8TD
Ground Capacity: 9,088
Seating Capacity: 6,322

Record Attendance: 9,077 (22nd September 2010)
Pitch Size: 112 × 72 yards
Colours: Shirts and shorts are Claret with Sky Blue trim
Telephone N°: (01724) 840139
Ticket Office: (01724) 747670 (www.sufctickets.com)
Fax Number: (01724) 857986
Web Site: www.scunthorpe-united.co.uk
E-mail: receptionist@scunthorpe-united.co.uk

GENERAL INFORMATION

Car Parking: Spaces for 800 cars at the ground
Coach Parking: At the ground
Nearest Railway Station: Scunthorpe (1½ miles)
Nearest Bus Station: Scunthorpe (1½ miles)
Club Shop: At the ground
Opening Times: Weekdays 8.30am to 5.00pm
Matchdays 9.00am to 3.00pm and 4.45pm to 5.15pm
Telephone N°: 0871 221-1899

GROUND INFORMATION

Away Supporters' Entrances & Sections:
Turnstiles 6-7 for the South Stand

ADMISSION INFO (2017/2018 PRICES)

Adult Standing: £18.00 – £22.00
Adult Seating: £20.00 – £24.00
Concessionary Standing: £13.00 – £16.00
Concessionary Seating: £13.00 – £16.00
Under-18s Standing: £6.00 – £9.00   (Under-12s free)
Under-18s Seating: £4.00 – £16.00
Note: Discounted prices are available for members
Programme Price: £3.00

FANS WITH DISABILITIES INFORMATION

Wheelchairs: 10 spaces for Home fans and 6 spaces for
Away fans in a special section in the Grove Wharf Stand
Helpers: One helper admitted per fan with disabilities
Prices: Normal prices for fans with disabilities. Helpers free
Disabled Toilets: Available
Commentaries are available for the blind
Contact: (01724) 747670   (Bookings are necessary)

Travelling Supporters' Information:
Routes: From All Parts: Exit the M180 at Junction 3 onto the M181. Follow the M181 to the roundabout with the A18 and take the A18 towards Scunthorpe – the ground is on the right after 200 yards.

SHEFFIELD UNITED FC

Founded: 1889 (**Entered League**: 1892)
Nickname: 'Blades'
Ground: Bramall Lane, Sheffield   S2 4SU
Ground Capacity: 32,609 (All seats)
Record Attendance: 68,287 (15th February 1936)
Pitch Size: 110 × 73 yards

Colours: Red and White striped shirts, Black shorts
Telephone Nº: (0114) 253-7200
Ticket Office: 0871 995-1889
Web Site: www.sufc.co.uk
E-mail: info@sufc.co.uk

GENERAL INFORMATION

Car Parking: Street parking only
Coach Parking: By Police direction
Nearest Railway Station: Sheffield Midland (1 mile)
Nearest Bus Station: Pond Street, Sheffield (1 mile)
Club Shop: At the ground
Opening Times: Monday to Friday and Matchdays from 9.00am to 5.00pm
Telephone Nº: (0114) 253-7200

GROUND INFORMATION

Away Supporters' Entrances & Sections:
Visitors' Box Office – Bramall Lane Stand Lower Tier

ADMISSION INFO (2017/2018 PRICES)

Adult Seating: £22.00 – £36.00
Under-18s Seating: £12.00 – £20.00
Young Adult/Student Seating: £14.00 – £24.00
Senior Citizen Seating: £16.00 – £29.00
Note: Prices vary depending on the category of the game and tickets are cheaper when purchased in advance
Programme Price: £4.00

FANS WITH DISABILITIES INFORMATION

Wheelchairs: Limited number of spaces available
Helpers: One helper admitted per wheelchair
Prices: Please contact the club for information
Disabled Toilets: 7 available within the enclosure
Commentaries available for the blind on request
Contact: (0114) 253-7200   (Bookings are necessary)

Travelling Supporters' Information:
Routes: From the North: Exit the M1 at Junction 33 following signs to Sheffield (A57) and continue along Sheffield Parkway until the Park Square roundabout. Take the 3rd exit and follow the A61 (Sheffield). Midland Station is on the left, the road veers to the left then take the middle lane following the ring road to the right. Take the first exit at the roundabout into Bramall Lane.; From the South: Exit the M1 at junction 29 and take the A617 (Chesterfield). Take the 3rd exit at the roundabout onto the A61 and continue to the Earl of Arundel and Surrey Public House. Turn left and continue into Bramall Lane; From the East: Exit the M1 at Junctions 31 or 33 and take the A57 to the roundabout, take the 3rd exit into Sheaf Street (then as from the North); From the West: Take the A57 into Sheffield and take the 4th exit at the roundabout into Upper Hanover Street and at the 2nd roundabout take the 3rd exit into Bramall Lane.

SHEFFIELD WEDNESDAY FC

Founded: 1867 (**Entered League**: 1892)
Former Name: The Wednesday FC
Nickname: 'Owls'
Ground: Hillsborough, Sheffield S6 1SW
Ground Capacity: 33,854 (All seats)
Record Attendance: 72,841 (17th February 1934)

Pitch Size: 116 × 75 yards
Colours: Blue shirts with White sleeves, Blue shorts
Telephone Nº: 03700 20-1867
Ticket Hotline: 03700 20-1867 Option 1
Web Site: www.swfc.co.uk
E-mail: enquiries@swfc.co.uk

GENERAL INFORMATION

Car Parking: Street parking
Coach Parking: Clay Wheels Lane
Nearest Railway Station: Sheffield Midland (4 miles)
Nearest Bus Station: Pond Street, Sheffield (4 miles)
Club Shop: At the ground
Ground Opening Times: Monday to Friday from 8.45am to 5.15pm and Saturday from 9.00am to 12.00pm
Telephone Nº: 03700 20-1867

GROUND INFORMATION

Away Supporters' Entrances & Sections:
West Stand turnstiles for West Stand, Upper Tier

ADMISSION INFO (2017/2018 PRICES)

Adult Seating: £25.00 – £49.00
Under-11s Seating: £10.00
Under-5s Seating: £5.00
Concessionary Seating: £15.00 – £39.00
Note: Prices vary according to the category of the game.

FANS WITH DISABILITIES INFORMATION

Wheelchairs: 91 spaces for home fans and 9 spaces for visiting fans in special sections in the North Stand, Kop Stand and West Stand Lower. Ambulant fans with disabilities can sit in any section of the ground other than the Grandstand.
Helpers: Admitted
Prices: Normal prices for the disabled. Helpers free of charge
Disabled Toilets: Available in the North and West Stands
Commentaries are available for the blind
Contact: 03700 20-1867 (Option 1) (Bookings are necessary)

Travelling Supporters' Information:
Routes: From the North, South and East: Exit the M1 at Junction 36 and follow signs to Sheffield (A61). Continue for 4 miles then take the 3rd exit at the 2nd roundabout into Leppings Lane. The ground is situated on the left; From the West: Take the A57 until the road splits in two. Take the left fork (A6101). After 3¾ miles turn left onto the one-way system and follow the road round to the right onto Holme Lane. This road becomes Bradfield Road. At the junction with the A61 (Penistone Road), turn left towards Barnsley. The stadium is on the left after Hillsborough Park.

SHREWSBURY TOWN FC

Founded: 1886 (**Entered League**: 1950)
Nickname: 'Town'
Ground: Greenhous Meadow Stadium, Oteley Road, Shrewsbury SY2 6ST
Ground Capacity: 9,875 (All seats)
Record Attendance: 18,917 (26th April 1961)
Pitch Size: 116 × 75 yards

Colours: Shirts and shorts are Blue with Amber and White trim
Telephone Nº: (01743) 289177
Ticket Office: (01743) 273943
Fax Number: (01743) 246942
Web Site: www.shrewsburytown.com
E-mail: info@shrewsburytown.co.uk

GENERAL INFORMATION

Car Parking: Limited parking at the stadium – Permit Holders only. Parking restrictions are imposted on matchdays with no parking allowed in the vicinity of the stadium. Visiting fans should use the Park & Ride Scheme – cost £2.00 per person for the return journey – see below
Coach Parking: At the stadium
Nearest Railway Station: Shrewsbury (2½ miles)
Nearest Bus Station: Raven Meadows, Shrewsbury
Club Shop: At the ground
Opening Times: Matchdays and Office Hours
Telephone Nº: (01743) 289177

GROUND INFORMATION

Away Supporters' Entrances & Sections:
North Stand entrances and accommodation

ADMISSION INFO (2017/2018 PRICES)

Adult Seating: £20.00 – £22.00
Concessionary Seating: £15.00 – £17.00
Ages 12 to 18 Seating: £8.00 – £12.00
Under-12s Seating: £6.00 – £10.00
Under-8s Seating: Free of charge
Note: Prices vary depending on the category of the game
Programme Price: £3.00

FANS WITH DISABILITIES INFORMATION

Wheelchairs: Spaces in the North, South and East Stands
Helpers: One helper admitted per fan with disabilities
Prices: £15.00 – £17.00 for fans with disabilities. Helpers are admitted free of charge
Disabled Toilets: Available throughout the ground
Contact: (01743) 273943   (Bookings are necessary)

Travelling Supporters' Information:
Park & Ride information: Buses run every 15 minutes from 12.30pm to 2.30pm on Saturday matchdays and 6.15pm to 7.30pm on matchdays in the week. Parking is free and the return bus journey is £2.00 per person. Buses return to the car parks immediately after the match finishes and car parks will remain open for one hour only. Car Park Locations:
Oxon Park and Ride Site: From the West and North West. At the junction of the A5 and the A458 (Churncote Roundabout) follow the signs A458 'Shrewsbury Town Centre'. Oxon Park and Ride Site is clearly signposted; **The Shirehall**: From all routes proceed along the A5 to Emstrey Island Roundabout into Shrewsbury, take the A5064 along London Road to the Column roundabout. Take the 3rd exit at the roundabout and the first right into the Shirehall Car Park; **Shirehall Overflow Car Park**: Follow directions to London Road as above. Before you reach the roundabout the car park is on the right-hand side. Proceed on foot to the Shirehall main car park for the bus.

SOUTHAMPTON FC

Founded: 1885 (**Entered League**: 1920)
Former Names: Southampton St. Mary's YMCA FC (1885-1897)
Nickname: 'Saints'
Ground: St. Mary's Stadium, Britannia Road, Southampton SO14 5FP
Ground Capacity: 32,689 (All seats)
Record Attendance: 32,363 (28th April 2012)

Pitch Size: 112 × 72 yards
Colours: Red and White shirts with Black shorts
Telephone Nº: 0845 688-9448
Ticket Office: 02381 780780
General Fax Number: 0845 688-9445
Web Site: www.saintsfc.co.uk
E-mail: sfc@saintsfc.co.uk

GENERAL INFORMATION
Car Parking: Park & Ride only – must be pre-booked
Coach Parking: By Police direction
Nearest Railway Station: Southampton Central
Nearest Bus Station: Western Esplanade
Club Shop: At the ground and also at West Quay
Opening Times: Monday to Friday 9.00am to 5.00pm and Saturdays 9.30am to 5.00pm
Telephone Nº: 0845 688-9335 or 0845 688-9433

GROUND INFORMATION
Away Supporters' Entrances & Sections:
Northam Stand

ADMISSION INFO (2017/2018 PRICES)
Adult Seating: £32.00 – £52.00
Concessionary Seating: £22.00 – £52.00
Ages 18 to 21 Seating: £19.00 – £52.00
Under-18s Seating: £16.00 – £52.00
Under-11s Seating: £8.00 – £52.00
Note: Prices vary depending on the category of the game
Programme Price: £3.00

FANS WITH DISABILITIES INFORMATION
Wheelchairs: 200 spaces in total for Home and Away fans throughout the ground
Helpers: One helper admitted per fan with disabilities
Prices: £32.00 – £39.00 (cheaper prices for younger fans)
Disabled Toilets: Available in all Stands
Contact: (02380 718601   (Bookings are necessary)
E-mail Contact: tickets@saintsfc.co.uk

Travelling Supporters' Information:
Routes: Although the ground is situated in the Melbourne Street/Marine Parade area of Southampton, no parking is available in the immediate vicinity except by special arrangement for Disabled supporters. There are a number of well-signposted Park and Ride car parks around the City and those designated for Away fans should be clearly marked.

SOUTHEND UNITED FC

Founded: 1906 (**Entered League**: 1920)
Former Name: Southend Athletic FC
Nickname: 'Shrimpers' 'Blues'
Ground: Roots Hall Ground, Victoria Avenue, Southend-on-Sea   SS2 6NQ
Ground Capacity: 12,163 (All seats)
Record Attendance: 31,033 (10th January 1979)

Pitch Size: 110 × 74 yards
Colours: Blue shirts with White shorts
Telephone N°: (01702) 304050
Ticket Office: 08444 770077
Fax Number: (01702) 304124
Web Site: www.southendunited.co.uk
E-mail: info@southend-united.co.uk

GENERAL INFORMATION

Car Parking: Car park at the ground for 450 cars – Season Ticket holders only. Otherwise use street parking
Coach Parking: Car park at the ground. Coach drivers should contact the club prior to the game
Nearest Railway Station: Prittlewell (¼ mile)
Nearest Bus Station: London Road, Southend
Club Shop: At the ground
Opening Times: Monday to Friday and Matchdays during office hours. Non-Match Saturdays 10.00am to 3.00pm
Telephone N°: (01702) 351117

GROUND INFORMATION

Away Supporters' Entrances & Sections:
North Stand turnstiles for North Stand seating

ADMISSION INFO (2017/2018 PRICES)

Adult Seating: £25.00   (£22.00 purchased in advance)
Young Person/Student Seating: £17.00 (£14.00 advance)
Junior Seating (Under-17s): £12.00 (£10.00 in advance)
Under-8s Seating: £5.00 (£4.00 purchased in advance)
Senior Citizen Seating: £18.00   (£15.00 in advance)
Note: Tickets are cheaper when purchased in advance and other discounts are available in the Family Enclosure.
Programme Price: £3.00

FANS WITH DISABILITIES INFORMATION

Wheelchairs: 20 spaces in total for Home and Away fans in a special section in the West Stand
Helpers: One helper admitted per fan with disabilities
Prices: Concessionary prices apply for fans with disabilities. Helpers receive complimentary tickets
Disabled Toilets: Available
Commentaries are available for the blind
Contact: 08444 770077   (Bookings are necessary)

Travelling Supporters' Information:
Routes: From the North and West: From the M25 take Junction 29 and follow the A127 to Southend. About 1 mile outside of Southend Town Centre, take the 3rd exit at the roundabout into Victoria Avenue for the ground; From the A13: Follow signs for Southend, turn left into West Road at Westcliff. At the end of West Road turn left into Victoria Avenue – the ground is on the left.

STEVENAGE FC

Founded: 1976
Former Names: None
Nickname: 'Boro'
Ground: Lamex Stadium, Broadhall Way, Stevenage, Hertfordshire   SG2 8RH
Record Attendance: 8,040   (25th January 1998)
Pitch Size: 110 × 70 yards

Colours: Red and White shirts with Red shorts
Telephone N°: (01438) 223223
Ground Capacity: 7,104
Seating Capacity: 3,404
Web site: www.stevenagefc.com
E-mail: info@stevenagefc.com

GENERAL INFORMATION

Car Parking: Fairlands Show Ground (opposite)
Coach Parking: None at the Stadium
Nearest Railway Station: Stevenage (1 mile)
Nearest Bus Station: Stevenage
Club Shop: At the ground
Opening Times: Monday 11.00am to 5.00pm, Wednesday 10.00am to 2.00pm and other weekdays 12.00pm to 6.00pm
Telephone N°: (01438) 223223

GROUND INFORMATION

Away Supporters' Entrances & Sections:
South Terrace entrances and accommodation

ADMISSION INFO (2017/2018 PRICES)

Adult Standing: £20.00
Adult Seating: £24.00
Ages 21 and Under Standing: £8.00 – £12.00
Ages 21 and Under Seating: £12.00 – £16.00
Under-12s Standing: £6.00
Under-12s Seating: £10.00
Concessionary Standing: £18.00
Concessionary Seating: £21.00
Note: Tickets are cheaper when purchased in advance
Programme Price: £3.00

FANS WITH DISABILITIES INFORMATION

Wheelchairs: 12 spaces available by the North Terrace
Helpers: Admitted
Prices: Concessionary prices apply for fans with disabilities. Free of charge for helpers
Disabled Toilets: Yes
Contact: (01438) 223223   (Bookings are necessary)

Travelling Supporters' Information:
Routes: Exit the A1(M) at Junction 7 and take the B197. The ground is on the right at the 2nd roundabout.
Bus Routes: SB4 and SB5

STOKE CITY FC

Founded: 1863 (**Entered League**: 1888)
Former Name: Stoke FC
Nickname: 'The Potters'
Ground: bet365 Stadium, Stanley Matthews Way, Stoke-on-Trent ST4 4EG
Ground Capacity: 30,089 (All seats – 2015/16))
Record Attendance: 28,218 (5th January 2002)

Pitch Size: 115 × 74 yards
Colours: Red and White striped shirts, White shorts
Telephone N°: (01782) 367598
Ticket Office: (01782) 367599
Fax Number: (01782) 592210
Web Site: www.stokecityfc.com
E-mail: info@stokecityfc.com

GENERAL INFORMATION

Car Parking: At the ground (bookings necessary). Also various car parks within 10 minutes walk
Coach Parking: At the ground
Nearest Railway Station: Stoke-on-Trent (1½ miles)
Nearest Bus Station: Glebe Street, Stoke-on-Trent
Club Shop: At the ground and at the Potteries Shopping Centre in Hanley
Opening Times: Monday to Friday 9.00am – 5.30pm and non-match Saturdays 9.00am–2.00pm. Weekend Matchdays 9.00am to kick-off then 30 minutes after the final whistle. Evening games 9.00am to kick-off and 30 minutes after the final whistle.
Telephone N°: (01782) 592242

GROUND INFORMATION

Away Supporters' Sections: Sharp Stand

ADMISSION INFO (2017/2018 PRICES)

Adult Seating: £25.00 – £50.00
Under-17s Seating: £15.00 – £27.00
Under-11s Seating: £8.00 – £24.00
Senior Citizen Seating: £19.00 – £35.00
Note: Prices vary depending on the category of the game
Programme Price: £3.50

FANS WITH DISABILITIES INFORMATION

Wheelchairs: 186 spaces available in total
Helpers: One helper admitted per disabled person
Prices: £19.00 to £35.00 for each disabled fan plus helper
Disabled Toilets: Available
Commentaries are available – phone for details
Contact: (01782) 367599 (Bookings are necessary)

Travelling Supporters' Information:
Routes: From the North, South and West: Exit the M6 at Junction 15 and take the A500 to Stoke-on-Trent then the A50 towards Derby/Uttoxeter (the bet365 Stadium is signposted and visible to the right). Once on the A50 take the fist exit, turn right at the traffic lights and cross over the flyover. Turn right at the first roundabout, left at the next roundabout and right at the third roundabout for the stadium; From the East: Take the A50 to Stoke-on-Trent and take the last turn-off (signposted for bet365 Stadium). Go straight on at the first roundabout then right at the second roundabout to reach the stadium.

SUNDERLAND AFC

Founded: 1879   (**Entered League**: 1890)
Former Names: Sunderland and District Teachers FC
Nickname: 'The Black Cats'
Ground: Stadium of Light, Sunderland   SR5 1SU
Ground Capacity: 49,000 (All seats)
Record Attendance: 48,355 (13th April 2002)
Pitch Size: 110 × 74 yards (101 × 68 metres)

Colours: Red and White striped shirts, Black shorts
Telephone Nº: 0371 911-1200
Ticket Office: 0371 911-1973
Fax Number: (0191) 551-5123
Web Site: www.safc.com
E-mail: enquiries@safc.com

GENERAL INFORMATION
Car Parking: Spaces for 1,100 cars (reserved)
Coach Parking: At the ground
Nearest Railway Station: Sunderland (1 mile)
Nearest Bus Station: Town Centre (1 mile)
Club Shop: At the Stadium, plus smaller stores in Sainsburys in Washington and Debenhams in Sunderland
Opening Times: Monday to Saturday 9.00am – 5.00pm
Telephone Nº: (0191) 551-5375

GROUND INFORMATION
Away Supporters' Entrances & Sections:
South Stand

ADMISSION INFO (2017/2018 PRICES)
Following the club's relegation from the Premier League, prices had not been announced for the 2017/2018 season when we went to print. Please contact the club for further information.
Programme Price: £3.00

FANS WITH DISABILITIES INFORMATION
Wheelchairs: 180 spaces in total throughout the stadium
Helpers: Admitted
Prices: Normal prices for fans with disabilities. Helpers free
Disabled Toilets: Available in all stands and Corporate areas
Contact: (0191) 551-5122   (Bookings are necessary)

Travelling Supporters' Information:
Routes: From All Parts: Exit the A1 at the A690 Durham/Sunderland exit. After approximately 4 miles turn left onto the A19 (signposted Tyne Tunnel). Keep in the left lane and take the slip road (signposted Washington/Sunderland) onto the bridge over the River Wear. Turn right onto the A1231 (signposted Washington/Sunderland), stay on this road going straight across 4 roundabouts into Sunderland. Continue straight through 2 sets of traffic lights and the Stadium car park is on the right, about 1 mile past the traffic lights.

SWANSEA CITY FC

Founded: 1912 (**Entered League**: 1920)
Former Name: Swansea Town FC (1912-1970)
Nickname: 'The Swans'
Ground: Liberty Stadium, Landore, Swansea, SA1 2FA
Ground Capacity: 20,750 (All seats)
Record Attendance: 32,796 (at the Vetch Field)

Pitch Size: 115 × 74 yards
Colours: White and Black shirts, shorts and socks
Telephone Nº: (01792) 616600
Ticket Office: 0844 815-6665
Fax Number: (01792) 616606
Web Site: www.swanseacity.net
E-mail: info@swanseacityfc.co.uk

GENERAL INFORMATION

Car Parking: Reserved parking only at the stadium but 3,000 spaces are available in a Park & Ride scheme just off Junction 45 of the M4.
Coach Parking: By Police direction
Nearest Railway Station: Swansea High Street (1½ miles)
Nearest Bus Station: Quadrant Depot (2½ miles)
Club Shop: At the ground
Opening Times: Monday to Saturday 9.00am – 5.00pm
Telephone Nº: 0871 222-3434

GROUND INFORMATION

Away Supporters' Entrances & Sections:
North Stand

ADMISSION INFO (2016/2017 PRICES)

Adult Seating: £35.00 – £45.00
Concessionary Seating: £17.50 – £22.50
Programme Price: £3.00

FANS WITH DISABILITIES INFORMATION

Wheelchairs: 250 spaces available in total for Home and Away fans together with 250 spaces for helpers
Helpers: One helper admitted per wheelchair
Prices: Normal prices apply for fans with disabilities. Free of charge for helpers
Disabled Toilets: Available
There are a number of disabled parking spaces available at the stadium
Contact: 0844 815-6665 (Bookings are necessary)

Travelling Supporters' Information:
Routes: From All Parts: Exit the M4 at Junction 45 and follow signs for Swansea (A4067). The stadium is clearly signposted.

SWINDON TOWN FC

Founded: 1881 (**Entered League**: 1920)
Nickname: 'Robins'
Ground: County Ground, County Road, Swindon, SN1 2ED
Ground Capacity: 14,983 (All seats)
Record Attendance: 32,000 (15th January 1972)
Pitch Size: 110 × 73 yards

Colours: Red shirts and shorts
Telephone Nº: 0871 876-1879
Ticket Office: 0871 876-1993
Fax Number: 0844 880-1112
Web Site: www.swindontownfc.co.uk

GENERAL INFORMATION

Car Parking: Town Centre
Coach Parking: Car park adjacent to the ground
Nearest Railway Station: Swindon (½ mile)
Nearest Bus Station: Swindon (½ mile)
Club Shop: The Swindon Town Superstore
Opening Times: Weekdays 9.00am – 5.00pm, Non-Matchday Saturdays 9.00am – 12.00pm and Saturday Matchdays 9.00am to 3.00pm
Telephone Nº: 0871 876-1993

GROUND INFORMATION

Away Supporters' Entrances & Sections:
Arkell's Stand turnstiles for the Stratton Bank

ADMISSION INFO (2017/2018 PRICES)

Adult Seating: £19.00 – £23.00
Concessionary Seating: £15.00 – £17.00
Under-21s Seating: £10.00
Under-18s Seating: £6.00
Under-11s Seating: £2.00
Note: A selection of family tickets are also available
Programme Price: £3.00

FANS WITH DISABILITIES INFORMATION

Wheelchairs: 56 spaces in total for Home and Away fans in a special section in front of Arkell's Stand
Helpers: One helper admitted with each fan in a wheelchair
Prices: £14.00–£19.00 for each fan with disabilities and helper
Disabled Toilets: Available
Commentaries are available for the blind
Contact: 0871 876-1993 (Bookings are necessary)

Travelling Supporters' Information:
Routes: From London, the East and the South: Exit the M4 at Junction 15 and take the A345 into Swindon along Queen's Drive. Take the 3rd exit at 'Magic Roundabout' into County Road; From the West: Exit the M4 at Junction 15 then as above; From the North: Take the M4 or A345/A420/A361 to the County Road roundabout, then as above.

TOTTENHAM HOTSPUR FC

Tottenham Hotspur FC are playing their matches at Wembley Stadium during the 2017/2018 season as construction on their new stadium is completed.

Founded: 1882 (**Entered League**: 1908)
Former Name: Hotspur FC (1882-1884)
Nickname: 'Spurs'
Temporary ground: Wembley National Stadium, Wembley, London   HA9 0WS
Seating Capacity: 90,000 over three tiers –
     Lower Tier: 34,303 seats
     Middle Tier: 16,532 seats
     Upper Tier: 39,165 seats

Colours: White shirts with Navy Blue shorts
Telephone Nº: 0344 499-5000
Ticket Office: 0344 844-0102
Fax Number: (020) 8365-5175
Web Site: www.tottenhamhotspur.com
E-mail: supporter.services@tottenhamhotspur.com

GENERAL INFORMATION

Car Parking: The stadium is a Public Transport Location and, as such, parking is only available for pre-accredited vehicles. Any spaces which are available must be pre-purchased from the following web site: www.wembleyofficialparking.com
Coach Travel: National Express operates coach routes from hundreds of towns and cities direct to the stadium for special events: www.nationalexpress.com/wembley
Rail & Tube Travel: Wembley Park station is on the Jubilee and Metropolitan tube lines; Wembley Stadium station is on the Chiltern mainline and Wembley Central station is served by the Bakerloo tube, London Overground and London Midland and Southern railway lines.
Local Bus Services: Services 18, 83, 92, 182 , 223 and 483 all travel to the stadium
Club Shop: Stores in Tottenham, Harlow, Enfield, Waltham Cross, Stevenage, Southend and Chelmsford (opening September 2017)
Opening Times: Varies from store to store. Generally open Monday to Saturday 9.30am – 5.30pm (open from 10.00am on Mondays). Also Sundays 10.00am – 4.30pm
Telephone Nº: 0344 499-5000

GROUND INFORMATION

Away Supporters' Entrances & Sections:
Turnstiles B and C (dependent on allocation taken by visiting club) – Blocks 112-117 are allocated for visiting supporters

ADMISSION INFO (2017/2018 PRICES)

Individual ticket prices for the 2017/2018 season had not been set at the time of going to press. Please contact the club for further ticketing details.

FANS WITH DISABILITIES INFORMATION

Wheelchairs: 310 spaces for wheelchairs are available in total alongside 310 seats for helpers. A further 100 enhanced amenity seats are available for ambulant visitors.
Helpers: One assistant is admitted free of charge with each supporter with disabilities.
Prices: Please contact the club for information
Disabled Toilets: Available throughout the stadium.
Contact: (020) 8365-5161   (Bookings are necessary)

WALSALL FC

Founded: 1888 (**Entered League**: 1892)
Former Name: Walsall Town Swifts FC (1888-1895)
Nickname: 'Saddlers'
Ground: Banks's Stadium, Bescot Crescent, Walsall, West Midlands WS1 4SA
Ground Capacity: 11,300 (All seats)
Record Attendance: 11,049 (9th May 2004)
Pitch Size: 110 × 73 yards

Colours: Red shirts with White shorts
Telephone Nº: (01922) 651410
Ticket Office: (01922) 651416 or (01922) 651414
Fax Number: (01922) 613202
Web Site: www.saddlers.co.uk
E-mail: info@walsallfc.co.uk

GENERAL INFORMATION

Car Parking: Car park at the ground
Coach Parking: At the ground
Nearest Railway Station: Bescot (adjacent)
Nearest Bus Station: Bradford Place, Walsall
Club Shop: At the ground
Opening Times: Weekdays 9.00am – 4.30pm and Saturday Matchdays 11.00am to 5.30pm
Telephone Nº: (01922) 651405

GROUND INFORMATION

Away Supporters' Entrances & Sections:
Turnstiles 21-28 for the University of Wolverhampton Stand

ADMISSION INFO (2017/2018 PRICES)

Adult Seating: £22.00 – £24.00
Child Seating: £14.00 – £16.00
Concessionary Seating: £16.00 – £18.00
Note: Discounts are available for advance bookings and savings from Family Tickets are available in some stands
Programme Price: £3.00

FANS WITH DISABILITIES INFORMATION

Wheelchairs: 33 spaces in total for Home and Away fans in the a special section in the St. Francis Group Community Stand
Helpers: One helper admitted with each fan with disabilities
Prices: Normal prices apply for fans with disabilities. Helpers are admitted free of charge
Disabled Toilets: Available
A special Lounge for fans with disabilities is available
Contact: (01922) 651416   (Bookings are necessary)

Travelling Supporters' Information:
Routes: From All Parts: Exit the M6 at Junction 9 turning North towards Walsall onto the A461. After ¼ mile turn right into Wallows Lane and pass over the railway bridge. Then take the 1st right into Bescot Crescent and the ground is ½ mile along on the left adjacent to Bescot Railway Station.

WATFORD FC

Photo courtesy of Alan Cozzi

Founded: 1881 (**Entered League**: 1920)
Former Names: Formed by the amalgamation of West Herts FC and St. Mary's FC
Nickname: 'Hornets'
Ground: Vicarage Road Stadium, Watford, WD18 0ER
Ground Capacity: 20,080 (All seats)
Record Attendance: 34,099 (3rd February 1969)

Pitch Size: 114 × 73 yards
Colours: Yellow & Black striped shirts, Black shorts
Telephone Nº: (01923) 496000
Ticket Office: (01923) 223023
Fax Number: (01923) 496001
Web Site: www.watfordfc.com
E-mail: yourvoice@watfordfc.com

GENERAL INFORMATION
Car Parking: Nearby multi-storey car parks and schools
Coach Parking: By Police direction
Nearest Railway Station: Watford Junction or Watford Tube Station (Metropolitan Line)
Nearest Bus Station: Watford Town Centre
Club Shop: The Hornets Shop at Vicarage Road Stadium
Opening Times: Monday to Saturday 9.30am to 5.30pm
Telephone Nº: (01923) 496000

GROUND INFORMATION
Away Supporters' Entrances & Sections:
Vicarage Road End entrances and accommodation

ADMISSION INFO (2017/2018 PRICES)
Adult Seating: £36.00 – £42.00
Under-16s Seating: £10.00 – £20.00
Young Adult/Student Seating: £18.00 – £24.00
Senior Citizen Seating: £22.00 – £28.00
Programme Price: £3.00

FANS WITH DISABILITIES INFORMATION
Wheelchairs: 51 spaces in total in special sections in the South East Corner, North East Corner and South West Corner
Helpers: One helper admitted with each fan with disabilities
Prices: Prices for fans with disabilities vary. Documentation is required when booking. Please contact the club for details
Disabled Toilets: Available
Commentaries available around the ground – no charge
Contact: (01923) 223003   (Bookings in advance helpful)

Travelling Supporters' Information:
Routes: From the North: Exit the M1 at Junction 5 and take the new road (A4008) towards Watford Town Centre. This will take you around the ring road, follow signs for Watford General Hospital. The ground is next to the hospital; From the South: Exit M1 at Junction 5 (then as North); From the East: Exit the M25 at Junction 21A and join the M1 at Junction 6. Exit at Junction 5 (then as North); From the West: Exit the M25 at Junction 19 and take the third exit off the roundabout onto the A411 (Hempstead Road) signposted for Watford. Continue for approximately two miles and go straight on at the roundabout (enter the right-hand lane) for the next roundabout and take the third exit into Rickmansworth Road. Take the second turning on the left into Cassio Road. Go through the traffic lights into Merton Road and follow signs for Watford General Hospital into Vicarage Road.

WEST BROMWICH ALBION FC

Founded: 1879 **(Entered League**: 1888)
Former Name: West Bromwich Strollers (1879-1880)
Nickname: 'Throstles' 'Baggies' 'Albion'
Ground: The Hawthorns, Halfords Lane,
West Bromwich, West Midlands B71 4LF
Ground Capacity: 26,850 (All seats)
Record Attendance: 64,815 (6th March 1937)

Pitch Size: 115 × 74 yards
Colours: Navy Blue & White striped shirts, White shorts
Telephone Nº: 0871 271-1100
Ticket Office: (0121) 227-2227
Fax Number: 0871 271-9861
Web Site: www.wba.co.uk
E-mail: enquiries@wbafc.co.uk

GENERAL INFORMATION

Car Parking: Halfords Lane Car Parks, East Stand Car Park and several independent car parks
Coach Parking: At the ground
Nearest Railway Station: Hawthorns (200 yards) or Rolfe Street, Smethwick (1½ miles)
Nearest Midland Metro: Hawthorns (200 yards)
Nearest Bus Station: West Bromwich Town Centre
Club Shop: At the ground and at the Merry Hill Centre
Opening Times: Weekdays 9.00am – 5.00pm and Saturday Matchdays 9.00am – 2.45pm
Telephone Nº: 0871 271-9790

GROUND INFORMATION

Away Supporters' Entrances & Sections:
Smethwick End 'A' turnstiles

ADMISSION INFO (2016/2017 PRICES)

Adult Seating: £25.00 – £39.00
Concessionary Seating: £20.00 – £29.00
Under-17s Seating: £10.00 – £15.00
Programme Price: £3.00

FANS WITH DISABILITIES INFORMATION

Wheelchairs: 150 spaces in total in special sections in the Birmingham Road End, Smethwick End and East Stand
Helpers: One helper admitted with each fan with disabilities (subject to availability of space)
Prices: £10.00 – £22.00 for fans with disabilities. Helpers free
Disabled Toilets: Available
Contact: 0871 271-1100 (Bookings are necessary)

Travelling Supporters' Information:
Routes: From All Parts: Exit the M5 at Junction 1 and follow Matchday signs for the ground. The matchday traffic plan has made the "obvious" route via the A41 unusable for home games.

WEST HAM UNITED FC

Photograph courtesy of Queen Elizabeth Olympic Park

Founded: 1895 (**Entered League**: 1919)
Former Name: Thames Ironworks FC
Nickname: 'Hammers'
Ground: London Stadium, Queen Elizabeth Olympic Park, Marsh Gate Lane, London   E20 2ST
Ground Capacity: 60,000 (All seats)
Record Attendance: 42,322 (Boleyn Ground, 1970)

Pitch Size: Not known
Colours: Claret and Blue shirts with White shorts
Telephone Nº: (020) 8548-2748
Ticket Office: 03330 301966
Web Site: www.whufc.com
E-mail: customerservices@westhamunited.co.uk

GENERAL INFORMATION

Car Parking: Limited spaces available at the Olympic Park. See Travelling Supporters' Information below for more details
Nearest Railway Station: Stratford (20 minutes walk)
Nearest Tube Station: Stratford (20 minutes walk)
Club Shops: At the Stadium and also at Lakeside Thurrock and Liberty Romford
Opening Times: Vary by store – please contact for details or check www.officialwesthamstore.com/page/find-a-store
Telephone Nº: (01708) 890258 (Lakeside Store) or (01708) 741877 (Liberty Romford)

GROUND INFORMATION

Away Supporters' Entrances & Sections:
Please contact the club for further details.

ADMISSION INFO (2017/2018 PRICES)

Please contact the club for details of ticket prices and availability for the 2017/2018 season.
Programme Price: £3.50

FANS WITH DISABILITIES INFORMATION

Wheelchairs: Spaces available throughout the stadium
Helpers: Admitted
Prices: Concessionary prices apply for fans with disabilities. Free of charge for helpers
Disabled Toilets: Available in all areas of the stadium
Contact: 03330 300174   (Bookings are necessary)

Travelling Supporters' Information:
Routes: Due to the fact that there is restricted car parking in the area of the stadium, it is recommended that visitors use the many public transport links available nearby, with tube and rail links plus numerous bus and coach routes close to the stadium. For those who choose to travel by car, the stadium is located in the Stratford area of east London, just to the east of the A12 and to the north of the River Thames. Visitors travelling by car are advised to use the public car parks at the Westfield Stratford City shopping centre, Stratford International station and the Stratford Centre.

WIGAN ATHLETIC FC

Founded: 1932 (**Entered League**: 1978)
Nickname: 'Latics'
Ground: DW Stadium, Loire Drive, Wigan, Lancashire   WN5 0UZ
Ground Capacity: 25,133 (All seats)
Record Attendance: 25,133 (11th May 2008)
Pitch Size: 115 × 74 yards

Colours: Blue and White striped shirts, Blue shorts
Telephone Nº: (01942) 774000
Ticket Office: 0871 66-33-552
Fax Number: (01942) 770477
Web Site: www.wiganlatics.co.uk
E-mail: feedback@wiganathletic.com

GENERAL INFORMATION

Car Parking: 2,500 spaces available at the ground (£4.00 for cars, £10.00 for minibuses, £20.00 for coaches)
Coach Parking: At the ground
Nearest Railway Station: Wallgate and Wigan North Western (1 mile)
Nearest Bus Station: Wigan
Club Shop: At the DW Stadium (matchdays only from 3 hours before kick-off) and also a store in Wigan Town Centre.
Opening Times: Monday to Saturday 9.00am to 5.30pm, Sundays and Bank Holidays 10.30am – 4.30pm
Telephone Nº: (01942) 248413

GROUND INFORMATION

Away Supporters' Entrances & Sections: North Stand

ADMISSION INFO (2017/2018 PRICES)

Adult Seating: £22.00 – £30.00
Senior Citizen Seating: £20.00 – £27.00
Under-18s Seating: £10.00 – £15.00
Under-11s Seating: £5.00 – £10.00   **Under-5s**: £2.00
Note: Prices vary depending on the category of the game. Discounted prices are available for advance purchases.
Programme Price: £3.00

FANS WITH DISABILITIES INFORMATION

Wheelchairs: 25 spaces available in each stand
Helpers: One helper admitted with each fan with disabilities
Prices: Please contact the club for information
Disabled Toilets: Available in every stand
Contact: 0871 663-3552   (Bookings are necessary)

Travelling Supporters' Information:
Routes: From North: Exit M6 at Junction 27, turn left at end of slip road then right at T-junction, signposted Shevington. After 1 mile turn left at the mini-roundabout into Old Lane (B5375). After approx. 2 miles winding through countryside turn right at traffic lights into Scot Lane. Stadium is next left; From South & West: Exit M6 at Junction 25 follow signs for Wigan (A49). After approx. 2 miles a complex junction is reached, keep in left-hand lane (McDonalds on right). Turn left at traffic light filter lane into Robin Park Road. Turn right at third set of traffic lights and follow road to stadium; From East: Exit M61 Junction 6, take 1st exit at roundabout. At next roundabout take 1st left into Chorley Road. Follow signs for Wigan B5238, first turning right then left at Aspull Roundabout. After 2 miles turn right at traffic lights after Earl of Balcarres Pub to face Tesco. Turn left at lights, keep in left lane turn left at next lights with the Quality Hotel on the corner. Follow ring road, get into second lane from right as road bears right into Caroline Street, signposted Orrell. Continue on ring road as it bears left passing B&Q on left, pass Wigan Pier on right and as road goes under railway bridge get into right hand lane to turn right at lights into Robin Park Road. Then South & West.

WOLVERHAMPTON WANDERERS FC

Founded: 1877 (**Entered League**: 1888)
Former Names: Formed by the amalgamation of St. Luke's FC and The Wanderers Football & Cricket Club in 1879. St. Luke's is considered the start of the club
Nickname: 'Wolves'
Ground: Molineux Stadium, Waterloo Road, Wolverhampton WV1 4QR
Ground Capacity: 31,700

Record Attendance: 61,315 (11th February 1939)
Pitch Size: 110 × 75 yards
Colours: Gold shirts with Black shorts
Telephone Nº: 0871 222-2220
Ticket Office: 0871 222-1877
Fax Number: (01902) 687006
Web Site: www.wolves.co.uk
E-mail: info@wolves.co.uk

GENERAL INFORMATION

Car Parking: Around West Park, Newhampton Road and rear of the Stan Cullis Stand. Also in City Centre (5 minutes walk)
Coach Parking: By Police direction
Nearest Railway Station: Wolverhampton (¾ mile)
Nearest Bus Station: Wolverhampton (¾ mile)
Club Shop: At the ground
Opening Times: Daily from 9.00am to 5.00pm
Telephone Nº: 0871 222-2220

GROUND INFORMATION

Away Supporters' Entrances & Sections:
Steve Bull Stand Lower Tier (turnstiles for Block 3)

ADMISSION INFO (2017/2018 PRICES)

Adult Seating: £25.00 – £30.00
Senior Citizen/Under-21s Seating: £15.00 – £18.00
Under-17s Seating: £12.00 – £15.00
Under-12s Seating: £5.00 – £12.00
Programme Price: £3.00

FANS WITH DISABILITIES INFORMATION

Wheelchairs: 104 spaces in total in special sections in the Stan Cullis Stand and Billy Wright Family Enclosure
Helpers: Admitted
Prices: Please contact the club for details
Disabled Toilets: At both ends of the Stan Cullis Stand
Contact: 0871 222-1877 (Bookings are necessary)

Travelling Supporters' Information:
Routes: From North: Exit M6 Junction 12. At island take 3rd exit onto A5 for Wolverhampton. At next island turn left onto A449. After 6 miles A449 passes under M54, carry straight on and at 6th roundabout (Five Ways) take 3rd exit into Waterloo Road. Molineux is 1 mile straight on; From South West: Exit M5 Junction 2, follow signs for Wolverhampton on A4123 for 8 miles to ring road. Turn left on ring road (follow Molineux Centre signs). Take 2nd exit at next 2 islands * Pass Bank's Brewery and Swimming Baths on left and turn left at next set of traffic lights. Molineux is 500 yards on right; From South/East: Exit M6 Junction 10, take A454 (via Willenhall) to Wolverhampton ring road. At first ring road island take 4th exit (A449 to Stafford). Straight on at next 2 sets of traffic lights. Filter right at third set of lights (Waterloo Road). Molineux is 500 yards on right; From West: Take A41 to Wolverhampton ring road roundabout. Turn left into the ring road. Then as from the South West *

WYCOMBE WANDERERS FC

Founded: 1887 (**Entered League**: 1993)
Nickname: 'The Blues' 'The Chairboys'
Ground: Adams Park, Hillbottom Road, Sands, High Wycombe   HP12 4HJ
Ground Capacity: 10,000
Seating Capacity: 8,250
Record Attendance: 9,971 (10th January 2007)

Pitch Size: 115 × 75 yards
Colours: Navy and Light Blue quarters with Navy shorts
Telephone Nº: (01494) 472100
Ticket Office: (01494) 441118
Fax Number: (01494) 441589
Web Site: www.wwfc.com
E-mail: wwfc@wwfc.com

GENERAL INFORMATION

Car Parking: Car park at the ground
Coach Parking: Car park at the ground
Nearest Railway Station: High Wycombe
Nearest Bus Station: High Wycombe
Club Shop: At the ground
Opening Times: Matchdays only
Telephone Nº: (01494) 455713

GROUND INFORMATION

Away Supporters' Entrances & Sections:
Dreams Stand (seating only)

ADMISSION INFO (2017/2018 PRICES)

Adult Standing: £15.00   **Adult Seating**: £17.00–£22.00
Under-16s Standing: £7.00
Under-16s Seating: £7.00 – £18.00
Senior Citizen Standing: £13.00   **Seating**: £15–£19
Student Standing: £11.00   **Seating**: £13.00 – £17.00
Note: A £2.00 discount is available for advance purchases
Programme Price: £3.00

FANS WITH DISABILITIES INFORMATION

Wheelchairs: 50 spaces in total available in special sections of the Family Stand and Away Stand
Helpers: One helper admitted per wheelchair
Prices: Full price for fans with disabilities. Free for helpers
Disabled Toilets: Available in the Family Stand
Commentaries are available for 5 people
Contact: (01494) 441118   (Bookings are not necessary)

Travelling Supporters' Information:
Routes: From All Parts: Exit the M40 at Junction 4 and take the A4010 following Aylesbury signs. Go straight on at 3 mini-roundabouts then bear sharp left at the 4th roundabout into Lane End Road. Fork right into Hillbottom Road at the next roundabout. The ground is at the end of the road. Hillbottom Road is on the Sands Industrial Estate; From the Town Centre: Take the A40 West and after 1½ miles turn left into Chapel Lane (after the traffic lights). Turn right then right again at the mini-roundabout into Lane End Road – then as above.

YEOVIL TOWN FC

Founded: 1895
Former Names: Yeovil & Petters United FC
Nickname: 'Glovers'
Ground: Huish Park Stadium, Lufton Way, Yeovil, Somerset BA22 8YF
Ground Capacity: 9,565 **Seating Capacity**: 5,309
Record Attendance: 9,527 (25th April 2008)

Pitch Size: 108 × 67 yards
Colours: Green and White shirts with White shorts
Telephone Nº: (01935) 423662
Ticket Office Nº: (01935) 847888
Fax Number: (01935) 847886
Web site: www.ytfc.net
E-mail: info@ytfc.net

GENERAL INFORMATION

Car Parking: Spaces for 1,000 cars at the ground
Coach Parking: At the ground
Nearest Railway Station: Yeovil Pen Mill (2½ miles) and Yeovil Junction (3½ miles)
Nearest Bus Station: Yeovil (2 miles)
Club Shop: At the ground
Opening Times: Weekdays 10.00am – 4.00pm and Matchdays 10.00am – 3.00pm
Telephone Nº: (01935) 847877

GROUND INFORMATION

Away Supporters' Entrances & Sections:
The Radio Cabs Stand (turnstiles 13-16) and Screwfix Community Stand (turnstile 12)

ADMISSION INFO (2017/2018 PRICES)

Adult Standing: £20.00
Adult Seating: £24.00 – £25.00
Under-16s Standing/Seating: £6.00
Ages 16 to 21 Standing/Seating: £16.00
Senior Citizen Standing: £18.00
Senior Citizen Seating: £20.00 – £22.00
Note: Discounted prices are available for tickets which are purchased before the day of the match.
Programme Price: £3.00

FANS WITH DISABILITIES INFORMATION

Wheelchairs: 15 spaces for home fans, 5 spaces for away fans
Helpers: Admitted free of charge
Prices: Please phone the club for information
Disabled Toilets: Two are available
Contact: (01935) 847888 (Bookings are recommended)

Travelling Supporters' Information:
Routes: From London: Take the M3 and A303 to Cartgate Roundabout. Enter Yeovil on the A3088. Exit left at the 1st roundabout then straight over the next two roundabouts into Western Avenue. Cross the next roundabout then turn left into Copse Road, where supporters' parking is sited; From the North: Exit the M5 at Junction 25 and take the A358 (Ilminster) and A303 (Eastbound) entering Yeovil on the A3088. Then as above.

F.A. Premier League 2016/2017 Season	Arsenal	AFC Bournemouth	Burnley	Chelsea	Crystal Palace	Everton	Hull City	Leicester City	Liverpool	Manchester City	Manchester United	Middlesbrough	Southampton	Stoke City	Sunderland	Swansea City	Tottenham Hotspur	Watford	West Bromwich Albion	West Ham United
Arsenal	■	3-1	2-1	3-0	2-0	3-1	2-0	1-0	3-4	2-2	2-0	0-0	2-1	3-1	2-0	3-2	1-1	1-2	1-0	3-0
AFC Bournemouth	3-3	■	2-1	1-3	0-2	1-0	6-1	1-0	4-3	0-2	1-3	4-0	1-3	2-2	1-2	2-0	0-0	2-2	1-0	3-2
Burnley	0-1	3-2	■	1-1	3-2	2-1	1-1	1-0	2-0	1-2	0-2	1-0	1-0	1-0	4-1	0-1	0-2	2-0	2-2	1-2
Chelsea	3-1	3-0	3-0	■	1-2	5-0	2-0	3-0	1-2	2-1	4-0	3-0	4-2	4-2	5-1	3-1	2-1	4-3	1-0	2-1
Crystal Palace	3-0	1-1	0-2	0-1	■	0-1	4-0	2-2	2-4	1-2	1-2	1-0	3-0	4-1	0-4	1-2	0-1	1-0	0-1	0-1
Everton	2-1	6-3	3-1	0-3	1-1	■	4-0	4-2	0-1	4-0	1-1	3-1	3-0	1-0	2-0	1-1	1-1	1-0	3-0	2-0
Hull City	1-4	3-1	1-1	0-2	3-3	2-2	■	2-1	2-0	0-3	0-1	4-2	2-1	0-2	0-2	2-1	1-7	2-0	1-1	2-1
Leicester City	0-0	1-1	3-0	0-3	3-1	0-2	3-1	■	3-1	4-2	0-3	2-2	0-0	2-0	2-0	2-1	1-6	3-0	1-2	1-0
Liverpool	3-1	2-2	2-1	1-1	1-2	3-1	5-1	4-1	■	1-0	0-0	3-0	0-0	4-1	2-0	2-3	2-0	6-1	2-1	2-2
Manchester City	2-1	4-0	2-1	1-3	5-0	1-1	3-1	2-1	1-1	■	0-0	1-1	1-1	0-0	2-1	2-1	2-2	2-0	3-1	3-1
Manchester United	1-1	1-1	0-0	2-0	2-0	1-1	0-0	4-1	1-1	1-2	■	2-1	2-0	1-1	3-1	1-1	1-0	2-0	0-0	1-1
Middlesbrough	1-2	2-0	0-0	0-1	1-2	0-0	1-0	0-0	0-3	2-2	1-3	■	1-2	1-1	1-0	3-0	1-2	0-1	1-1	1-3
Southampton	0-2	0-0	3-1	0-2	3-1	1-0	0-0	3-0	0-0	0-3	0-0	1-0	■	0-1	1-1	1-0	1-4	1-1	1-2	1-3
Stoke City	1-4	0-1	2-0	1-2	1-0	1-1	3-1	2-2	1-2	1-4	1-1	2-0	0-0	■	2-0	3-1	0-4	2-0	1-1	0-0
Sunderland	1-4	0-1	0-0	0-1	2-3	0-3	3-0	2-1	2-2	0-2	0-3	1-2	0-4	1-3	■	0-2	0-0	1-0	1-1	2-2
Swansea City	0-4	0-3	3-2	2-2	5-4	1-0	0-2	2-0	1-2	1-3	1-3	0-0	2-1	2-0	3-0	■	1-3	0-0	2-1	1-4
Tottenham Hotspur	2-0	4-0	2-1	2-0	1-0	3-2	3-0	1-1	1-1	2-0	2-1	1-0	2-1	4-0	1-0	5-0	■	4-0	4-0	3-2
Watford	1-3	2-2	2-1	1-2	1-1	3-2	1-0	2-1	0-1	0-5	3-1	0-0	3-4	0-1	1-0	1-0	1-4	■	2-0	1-1
West Bromwich Albion	3-1	2-1	4-0	0-1	0-2	1-2	3-1	0-1	0-1	0-4	0-2	0-0	0-1	1-0	2-0	3-1	1-1	3-1	■	4-2
West Ham United	1-5	1-0	1-0	1-2	3-0	0-0	1-0	2-3	0-4	0-4	0-2	1-1	0-3	1-1	1-0	1-0	1-0	2-4	2-2	■

EFL Championship 2016/2017 Season

	Aston Villa	Barnsley	Birmingham City	Blackburn Rovers	Brentford	Brighton & Hove Albion	Bristol City	Burton Albion	Cardiff City	Derby County	Fulham	Huddersfield Town	Ipswich Town	Leeds United	Newcastle United	Norwich City	Nottingham Forest	Preston North End	Queen's Park Rangers	Reading	Rotherham United	Sheffield Wednesday	Wigan Athletic	Wolverhampton Wanderers
Aston Villa	■	1-3	1-0	2-1	1-1	1-1	2-0	2-1	3-1	1-0	1-0	1-1	0-1	1-1	1-1	2-0	2-2	2-2	1-0	1-3	3-0	2-0	1-0	1-1
Barnsley	1-1	■	2-2	2-0	1-1	0-2	2-2	1-1	0-0	2-0	2-4	1-1	1-1	3-2	0-2	2-1	2-5	0-0	3-2	1-2	4-0	1-1	0-0	1-3
Birmingham City	1-1	0-3	■	1-0	1-3	1-2	1-0	0-2	0-0	1-2	1-0	2-0	2-1	1-3	0-0	3-0	0-0	2-2	1-4	0-1	4-2	2-1	0-1	1-3
Blackburn Rovers	1-0	0-2	1-1	■	3-2	2-3	1-1	2-2	1-1	1-0	0-1	1-1	0-0	1-2	1-0	1-4	2-1	2-2	1-0	2-3	4-2	0-1	1-0	1-1
Brentford	3-0	0-2	1-2	1-3	■	3-3	2-0	2-1	2-2	4-0	0-2	0-1	2-0	2-0	1-2	0-0	1-0	5-0	3-1	4-1	4-2	1-1	0-0	1-2
Brighton & Hove Albion	1-1	2-0	3-1	1-0	0-2	■	0-1	4-1	1-0	3-0	2-1	1-0	1-1	2-0	1-2	5-0	3-0	2-2	3-0	3-0	3-0	2-1	2-1	1-0
Bristol City	3-1	3-2	0-1	1-0	0-1	0-2	■	0-0	2-3	1-1	0-2	4-0	2-0	0-1	1-1	2-1	1-2	2-1	2-3	1-0	2-2	2-1	3-1	
Burton Albion	1-1	0-0	2-0	1-1	3-5	0-1	1-2	■	2-0	1-0	0-2	0-1	1-2	2-1	1-2	2-1	1-0	0-1	1-1	2-4	2-1	3-1	0-2	2-1
Cardiff City	1-0	3-4	1-1	2-1	2-1	0-0	2-1	1-0	■	0-2	2-2	3-2	3-1	0-2	0-2	0-1	1-0	2-0	0-2	0-1	5-0	1-1	0-1	2-1
Derby County	0-0	2-1	1-0	1-2	0-0	0-0	3-3	0-0	3-4	■	4-2	1-1	0-1	1-0	0-2	1-0	3-0	1-1	1-0	3-2	3-0	2-0	0-0	3-1
Fulham	3-1	2-0	0-1	2-2	1-1	1-2	0-4	1-1	2-2	2-2	■	5-0	3-1	1-1	1-0	2-2	3-2	3-1	1-2	5-0	2-1	1-1	3-2	1-3
Huddersfield Town	1-0	2-1	1-1	1-1	2-1	3-1	2-1	0-1	0-3	1-0	1-4	■	2-0	2-1	1-3	3-0	2-1	3-2	2-1	1-0	2-1	0-1	1-2	1-0
Ipswich Town	0-0	4-2	1-1	3-2	1-1	0-0	2-1	2-0	1-1	0-3	0-2	0-1	■	1-1	3-1	1-1	0-2	1-0	3-0	2-2	2-2	0-1	3-0	0-0
Leeds United	2-0	2-1	1-2	2-1	1-0	2-0	2-1	2-0	0-2	1-0	1-1	0-1	1-0	■	0-2	3-3	2-0	3-0	0-0	2-0	3-0	1-0	1-1	0-1
Newcastle United	2-0	3-0	4-0	0-1	3-1	2-0	2-2	1-0	2-1	1-0	1-3	1-2	3-0	1-1	■	4-3	3-1	4-1	2-2	4-1	4-0	0-1	2-1	0-2
Norwich City	1-0	2-0	2-0	2-2	5-0	2-0	1-0	3-1	3-2	3-0	1-3	1-2	1-1	2-3	2-2	■	5-1	0-1	4-0	7-1	3-1	0-0	2-1	3-1
Nottingham Forest	2-1	0-1	3-1	0-1	2-3	3-0	1-0	4-3	1-2	2-2	1-1	2-0	3-0	3-1	2-1	1-2	■	1-1	1-1	3-2	2-0	1-2	4-3	0-2
Preston North End	2-0	1-2	2-1	3-2	4-2	2-0	5-0	1-1	3-0	0-1	1-2	3-1	1-1	1-4	1-2	1-3	1-1	■	2-1	3-0	1-1	1-1	1-0	0-0
Queens Park Rangers	0-1	2-1	1-1	1-1	0-2	1-2	1-0	1-2	2-1	0-1	1-1	1-2	2-1	3-0	0-6	2-1	2-0	0-2	■	1-1	5-1	1-2	2-1	1-2
Reading	1-2	0-0	0-0	3-1	3-2	2-2	2-1	3-0	2-1	1-1	1-0	1-0	2-1	1-0	0-0	3-1	2-0	1-0	0-1	■	2-1	2-1	1-0	2-1
Rotherham United	0-2	0-1	1-1	1-1	1-0	0-2	2-2	1-2	1-2	1-1	0-1	2-3	1-0	1-2	0-1	2-2	1-3	0-1	0-1		■	0-2	3-2	2-2
Sheffield Wednesday	1-0	2-0	3-0	2-1	1-2	1-2	3-2	1-1	1-0	2-1	1-2	2-0	1-2	0-2	2-1	5-1	2-1	2-1	1-0	0-2	1-0	■	2-1	0-0
Wigan Athletic	0-2	3-2	1-1	3-0	2-1	0-1	0-1	0-0	0-0	0-1	0-0	0-1	2-3	1-1	0-2	2-2	0-0	0-0	0-1	0-3	3-2	0-1	■	2-1
Wolverhampton Wanderers	1-0	0-4	1-2	0-0	3-1	0-2	3-2	1-1	3-1	2-3	4-4	0-1	0-0	0-1	1-2	1-0	1-0	1-2	2-0	1-0	0-2	0-1	■	

EFL League One 2016/2017 Season	AFC Wimbledon	Bolton Wanderers	Bradford City	Bristol Rovers	Bury	Charlton Athletic	Chesterfield	Coventry City	Fleetwood Town	Gillingham	Millwall	Milton Keynes Dons	Northampton Town	Oldham Athletic	Oxford United	Peterborough United	Port Vale	Rochdale	Scunthorpe United	Sheffield United	Shrewsbury Town	Southend United	Swindon Town	Walsall
AFC Wimbledon		1-2	2-3	0-1	5-1	1-1	2-1	1-1	2-2	2-0	2-2	2-0	0-1	0-0	2-1	0-0	4-0	3-1	1-2	2-3	1-1	0-2	0-0	1-0
Bolton Wanderers	1-1		0-0	1-1	0-0	1-2	0-0	1-0	2-1	4-0	2-0	1-1	2-1	2-0	0-2	3-0	3-1	1-0	2-1	1-0	2-1	1-1	1-2	4-1
Bradford City	3-0	2-2		1-1	1-1	0-0	2-0	3-1	2-1	2-2	1-1	2-2	1-0	1-1	1-0	1-0	0-0	4-0	0-0	3-3	2-0	1-1	2-1	1-0
Bristol Rovers	2-0	1-2	1-1		4-2	1-5	2-1	4-1	2-1	2-1	3-4	0-0	5-0	1-0	2-1	1-2	2-1	2-2	1-1	0-0	2-0	2-0	1-0	1-1
Bury	1-2	0-2	0-2	3-0		2-0	2-1	2-1	0-0	1-2	2-3	0-0	3-0	0-1	2-3	5-1	4-1	0-1	1-2	1-3	2-1	1-4	1-0	3-3
Charlton Athletic	1-2	1-1	1-1	4-1	0-1		1-0	3-0	1-1	3-0	0-0	0-2	1-1	1-1	0-2	2-0	0-1	2-1	1-1	3-0	2-1	3-0	1-1	
Chesterfield	0-0	1-0	0-1	3-2	1-2	1-2		1-0	0-1	3-3	1-3	0-0	3-1	0-1	0-4	3-3	1-0	1-3	0-3	1-4	1-1	0-4	3-1	2-0
Coventry City	2-2	2-2	0-2	1-0	0-0	1-1	2-0		0-1	2-1	0-2	1-2	1-1	0-0	2-1	1-0	2-1	2-0	0-1	1-2	0-0	0-2	1-3	1-0
Fleetwood Town	0-0	2-4	2-1	3-1	0-0	2-2	2-1	2-0		2-1	1-0	1-4	3-0	1-0	2-0	2-0	0-0	0-0	2-2	1-1	3-0	1-1	0-1	2-1
Gillingham	2-2	0-4	1-1	3-1	2-1	1-1	1-1	2-1	2-3		1-1	1-0	2-1	1-2	0-1	0-1	1-1	3-0	3-2	1-2	1-1	2-1	1-1	1-1
Millwall	0-0	0-2	1-1	4-0	0-0	3-1	0-0	1-1	2-1	2-1		2-1	3-0	3-0	0-3	1-0	2-0	2-3	3-1	2-1	0-1	1-0	2-0	0-0
Milton Keynes Dons	1-0	1-1	1-2	3-3	1-3	0-1	2-3	1-0	0-1	3-2	2-2		5-3	1-0	0-0	0-2	0-1	2-2	1-1	0-3	2-1	0-3	3-2	1-1
Northampton Town	0-0	0-1	1-2	2-3	3-2	2-1	3-1	3-0	1-1	0-0	1-3	3-2		1-2	0-0	0-1	2-1	2-3	1-2	1-2	1-1	4-0	2-1	2-0
Oldham Athletic	0-0	1-0	1-2	0-2	0-0	1-0	0-0	3-2	2-0	1-0	0-0	0-2	0-0		2-1	2-0	0-0	1-1	2-0	1-1	2-3	0-2	0-2	0-0
Oxford United	1-3	2-4	1-0	0-2	5-1	1-1	1-1	4-1	1-3	1-0	1-2	1-0	0-1	1-1		2-1	2-0	1-0	2-1	2-3	2-0	0-2	2-0	0-0
Peterborough United	0-1	1-0	0-1	4-2	3-1	2-0	5-2	1-1	1-2	1-1	5-1	0-4	3-0	1-1	1-2		2-2	3-1	0-2	0-1	2-1	1-4	2-2	1-1
Port Vale	2-0	0-2	1-2	1-1	2-2	1-1	1-0	0-2	2-1	2-1	3-1	0-0	2-3	2-2	2-2	0-3		1-0	3-1	0-3	2-1	2-0	3-2	0-1
Rochdale	1-1	1-0	1-1	0-0	2-0	3-3	3-0	2-0	2-1	4-1	3-3	0-1	1-1	1-0	0-4	2-3	3-0		3-2	3-3	2-1	3-0	4-0	4-0
Scunthorpe United	1-2	1-0	3-2	3-1	3-2	0-0	3-1	3-1	0-2	5-0	3-0	2-1	1-1	1-0	1-1	1-1	3-2	2-1		2-2	0-1	4-0	4-1	0-0
Sheffield United	4-0	2-0	3-0	1-0	1-0	2-1	3-2	2-0	0-2	2-2	2-0	2-1	1-0	2-0	2-1	1-0	4-0	1-1	1-1		2-1	0-3	4-0	0-1
Shrewsbury Town	2-1	0-2	1-0	2-0	2-1	4-3	2-1	0-0	0-1	2-3	1-2	0-1	2-4	1-0	2-0	1-1	0-0	1-0	0-1	0-3		1-0	1-1	1-1
Southend United	3-0	0-1	3-0	1-1	1-0	1-1	1-0	3-1	0-2	1-3	3-1	1-2	2-2	3-0	2-1	1-1	1-1	2-1	3-1	2-4	1-1		1-1	3-2
Swindon Town	0-0	0-1	1-0	1-2	1-2	3-0	0-1	1-0	1-1	3-1	1-0	1-1	1-3	0-0	1-2	0-1	1-0	3-0	1-2	2-4	1-1	0-0		0-2
Walsall	3-1	1-0	1-1	3-1	3-3	1-2	1-0	1-1	0-1	1-2	2-1	1-4	2-1	2-0	1-1	2-0	0-1	0-2	1-4	4-1	3-2	0-0	1-0	

EFL League Two 2016/2017 Season

	Accrington Stanley	Barnet	Blackpool	Cambridge United	Carlisle United	Cheltenham Town	Colchester United	Crawley Town	Crewe Alexandra	Doncaster Rovers	Exeter City	Grimsby Town	Hartlepool United	Leyton Orient	Luton Town	Mansfield Town	Morecambe	Newport County	Notts County	Plymouth Argyle	Portsmouth	Stevenage	Wycombe Wanderers	Yeovil Town
Accrington Stanley	■	1-0	2-1	2-0	1-1	1-1	2-1	1-0	3-2	3-2	1-2	1-1	2-2	5-0	1-4	1-1	2-3	1-3	2-0	0-1	1-0	0-1	2-2	1-1
Barnet	2-0	■	1-1	0-1	0-1	3-1	1-1	2-2	0-0	1-3	1-4	3-1	3-2	0-0	0-1	0-2	2-2	0-0	3-2	1-0	1-1	1-2	0-2	2-2
Blackpool	0-0	2-2	■	1-1	2-2	3-0	1-1	0-0	2-2	4-2	2-0	1-3	2-1	3-1	0-2	0-1	3-1	4-1	4-0	0-1	3-1	1-0	0-0	2-2
Cambridge United	2-1	1-1	0-0	■	2-2	3-1	1-1	2-0	2-1	2-3	1-0	0-1	0-1	3-0	0-3	1-3	1-2	3-2	4-0	0-1	0-1	0-0	1-2	1-0
Carlisle United	1-1	1-1	1-4	0-3	■	1-1	2-0	3-1	0-2	2-1	3-2	1-3	3-2	2-2	0-0	5-2	1-1	2-1	1-2	1-0	0-3	1-1	1-0	2-1
Cheltenham Town	3-0	1-2	2-2	0-1	1-0	■	0-3	2-1	2-0	0-1	1-3	2-1	1-0	1-1	1-1	0-0	3-1	1-1	2-3	1-2	1-1	0-0	0-1	2-0
Colchester United	1-2	2-1	3-2	2-0	4-1	2-0	■	2-3	4-0	1-1	2-3	3-2	2-1	0-3	2-1	2-0	2-2	0-0	2-1	0-0	0-4	4-0	1-0	2-0
Crawley Town	0-0	1-1	1-0	1-3	3-3	0-0	1-1	■	0-3	0-0	1-2	3-2	1-0	3-0	2-0	2-2	1-3	3-1	1-3	1-2	0-2	1-2	1-0	2-0
Crewe Alexandra	0-1	4-1	1-1	1-2	1-1	0-0	2-0	0-2	■	2-1	2-0	5-0	3-3	3-0	1-2	1-1	2-1	1-2	2-2	1-2	0-0	1-2	2-1	0-1
Doncaster Rovers	2-2	3-2	0-1	1-0	2-2	2-0	1-0	1-1	3-1	■	1-3	1-0	2-1	3-1	1-1	1-0	1-1	2-0	3-1	0-1	3-1	1-0	2-2	4-1
Exeter City	0-2	2-1	2-2	1-2	2-3	3-0	3-0	0-1	4-0	1-3	■	0-0	1-2	4-0	0-0	2-0	3-1	0-1	0-2	0-2	0-1	1-1	4-2	3-3
Grimsby Town	2-0	2-2	0-0	2-1	2-2	0-1	1-0	1-1	0-2	1-5	0-3	■	0-3	1-2	1-1	3-0	2-0	1-0	2-0	1-1	0-1	5-2	1-2	4-2
Hartlepool United	2-0	0-2	0-1	0-5	1-1	2-0	1-1	1-1	4-0	2-1	3-1	0-1	■	1-3	1-1	0-0	3-2	2-2	1-2	1-1	0-2	2-0	0-2	1-1
Leyton Orient	1-0	1-3	1-2	1-1	1-2	0-1	1-3	3-2	0-2	1-4	0-1	0-3	2-1	■	1-2	1-2	0-1	0-1	2-3	0-2	0-1	3-0	0-2	0-1
Luton Town	1-0	3-1	1-0	2-0	1-1	2-3	0-1	2-1	1-1	3-1	1-1	1-2	3-0	2-2	■	1-1	3-1	2-1	2-1	1-1	1-3	0-2	4-1	1-1
Mansfield Town	4-4	0-1	1-0	0-0	2-0	1-1	0-0	3-1	3-0	1-1	1-2	0-1	4-0	2-0	1-1	■	0-1	2-1	3-1	0-2	0-1	1-2	1-1	1-0
Morecambe	1-2	0-1	2-1	2-0	0-3	1-2	1-1	2-3	0-0	1-5	0-3	1-0	1-1	1-2	0-2	1-3	■	0-1	4-1	2-1	2-0	0-2	1-1	1-3
Newport County	1-0	2-2	1-3	1-2	2-0	2-2	1-1	1-0	1-1	0-0	1-4	0-0	3-1	0-4	1-1	2-3	1-1	■	2-1	1-3	2-3	0-2	0-1	1-0
Notts County	0-2	1-0	1-0	0-1	2-3	2-1	3-1	2-1	1-1	2-2	2-2	2-1	3-1	0-0	0-0	1-2	0-3		■	1-2	1-3	1-1	0-2	0-0
Plymouth Argyle	0-1	0-2	0-3	2-1	2-0	1-0	2-1	2-0	2-1	2-0	3-0	0-3	1-1	2-3	0-3	2-0	1-0	6-1	0-1	■	2-2	4-2	3-3	4-1
Portsmouth	2-0	5-1	2-0	2-1	1-1	6-1	2-0	3-0	0-1	1-2	0-1	4-0	0-0	2-1	1-0	4-0	1-1	2-1	1-2	1-1	■	1-2	4-2	3-1
Stevenage	0-3	1-0	0-2	1-2	1-2	2-1	2-4	2-1	1-2	3-4	0-2	2-0	6-1	4-1	2-1	0-1	3-1	3-0	1-2	3-0		■	3-0	2-2
Wycombe Wanderers	1-1	0-2	0-0	1-0	1-2	3-3	0-2	1-2	5-1	2-1	1-0	2-1	2-0	1-0	1-1	0-1	2-0	2-1	0-1	1-1	1-0	1-0	■	1-1
Yeovil Town	1-1	0-1	0-3	1-1	0-2	4-2	2-1	5-0	3-0	0-3	0-0	0-0	1-2	1-1	0-4	0-0	0-1	1-0	2-0	2-1	0-0	1-1	1-0	■

F.A. Premier League

Season 2016/2017

Chelsea	38	30	3	5	85	33	93
Tottenham Hotspur	38	26	8	4	86	26	86
Manchester City	38	23	9	6	80	39	78
Liverpool	38	22	10	6	78	42	76
Arsenal	38	23	6	9	77	44	75
Manchester United	38	18	15	5	54	29	69
Everton	38	17	10	11	62	44	61
Southampton	38	12	10	16	41	48	46
AFC Bournemouth	38	12	10	16	55	67	46
West Bromwich Albion	38	12	9	17	43	51	45
West Ham United	38	12	9	17	47	64	45
Leicester City	38	12	8	18	48	63	44
Stoke City	38	11	11	16	41	56	44
Crystal Palace	38	12	5	21	50	63	41
Swansea City	38	12	5	21	45	70	41
Burnley	38	11	7	20	39	55	40
Watford	38	11	7	20	40	68	40
Hull City	38	9	7	22	37	80	34
Middlesbrough	38	5	13	20	27	53	28
Sunderland	38	6	6	26	29	69	24

Champions: Chelsea

Relegated: Hull City, Middlesbrough and Sunderland

Football League – The Championship

Season 2016/2017

Newcastle United	46	29	7	10	85	40	94
Brighton & Hove Albion	46	28	9	9	74	40	93
Reading	46	26	7	13	68	64	85
Sheffield Wednesday	46	24	9	13	60	45	81
Huddersfield Town	46	25	6	15	56	58	81
Fulham	46	22	14	10	85	57	80
Leeds United	46	22	9	15	61	47	75
Norwich City	46	20	10	16	85	69	70
Derby County	46	18	13	15	54	50	67
Brentford	46	18	10	18	75	65	64
Preston North End	46	16	14	16	64	63	62
Cardiff City	46	17	11	18	60	61	62
Aston Villa	46	16	14	16	47	48	62
Barnsley	46	15	13	18	64	67	58
Wolverhampton Wanderers	46	16	10	20	54	58	58
Ipswich Town	46	13	16	17	48	58	55
Bristol City	46	15	9	22	60	66	54
Queens Park Rangers	46	15	8	23	52	66	53
Birmingham City	46	13	14	19	45	64	53
Burton Albion	46	13	13	20	49	63	52
Nottingham Forest	46	14	9	23	62	72	51
Blackburn Rovers	46	12	15	19	53	65	51
Wigan Athletic	46	10	12	24	40	57	42
Rotherham United	46	5	8	33	40	98	23

Promotion Play-offs

Fulham 1   Reading 1
Huddersfield Town 0   Sheffield Wednesday 0

Reading 0   Fulham 0
Reading won 2-1 on aggregate.
Sheffield Wednesday 1   Huddersfield Town .... 1 (aet)
Aggregate 1-1. Huddersfield Town won 4-3 on penalties

Huddersfield Town 0   Reading .... 0 (aet)
Huddersfield Town won 4-3 on penalties

Promoted: Newcastle United, Brighton & Hove Albion and Huddersfield Town

Relegated: Blackburn Rovers, Wigan Athletic and Rotherham United

Football League – League One

Season 2016/2017

Sheffield United	46	30	10	6	92	47	100
Bolton Wanderers	46	25	11	10	68	36	86
Scunthorpe United	46	24	10	12	80	54	82
Fleetwood Town	46	23	13	10	64	43	82
Bradford City	46	20	19	7	62	43	79
Millwall	46	20	13	13	66	57	73
Southend United	46	20	12	14	70	53	72
Oxford United	46	20	9	17	65	52	69
Rochdale	46	19	12	15	71	62	69
Bristol Rovers	46	18	12	16	68	70	66
Peterborough United	46	17	11	18	62	62	62
Milton Keynes Dons	46	16	13	17	60	58	61
Charlton Athletic	46	14	18	14	60	53	60
Walsall	46	14	16	16	51	58	58
AFC Wimbledon	46	13	18	15	52	55	57
Northampton Town	46	14	11	21	60	73	53
Oldham Athletic	46	12	17	17	31	44	53
Shrewsbury Town	46	13	12	21	46	63	51
Bury	46	13	11	22	61	73	50
Gillingham	46	12	14	20	59	79	50
Port Vale	46	12	13	21	45	70	49
Swindon Town	46	11	11	24	44	66	44
Coventry City	46	9	12	25	37	68	39
Chesterfield	46	9	10	27	43	78	37

Promotion Play-offs

Millwall	0	Scunthorpe United	0
Bradford City	1	Fleetwood Town	0

Scunthorpe United	2	Millwall	3

Millwall won 3-2 on aggregate.

Fleetwood Town	0	Bradford City	0

Bradford City won 1-0 on aggregate.

Bradford City	0	Millwall	1

Promoted: Sheffield United, Bolton Wanderers and Millwall

Relegated: Port Vale, Swindon Town, Coventry City and Chesterfield

---

Football League – League Two

Season 2016/2017

Portsmouth	46	26	9	11	79	40	87
Plymouth Argyle	46	26	9	11	71	46	87
Doncaster Rovers	46	25	10	11	85	55	85
Luton Town	46	20	17	9	70	43	77
Exeter City	46	21	8	17	75	56	71
Carlisle United	46	18	17	11	69	68	71
Blackpool	46	18	16	12	69	46	70
Colchester United	46	19	12	15	67	57	69
Wycombe Wanderers	46	19	12	15	58	53	69
Stevenage	46	20	7	19	67	63	67
Cambridge United	46	19	9	18	58	50	66
Mansfield Town	46	17	15	14	54	50	66
Accrington Stanley	46	17	14	15	59	56	65
Grimsby Town	46	17	11	18	59	63	62
Barnet	46	14	15	17	57	64	57
Notts County	46	16	8	22	54	76	56
Crewe Alexandra	46	14	13	19	58	67	55
Morecambe	46	14	10	22	53	73	52
Crawley Town	46	13	12	21	53	71	51
Yeovil Town	46	11	17	18	49	64	50
Cheltenham Town	46	12	14	20	49	69	50
Newport County	46	12	12	22	51	73	48
Hartlepool United	46	11	13	22	54	75	46
Leyton Orient	46	10	6	30	47	87	36

Promotion Play-offs

Blackpool	3	Luton Town	2
Carlisle United	3	Exeter City	3

Luton Town	3	Blackpool	3

Blackpool won 6-5 on aggregate.

Exeter City	3	Carlisle United	2

Exeter City won 6-5 on aggregate.

Blackpool	2	Exeter City	1

Promoted: Portsmouth, Plymouth Argyle, Doncaster Rovers and Blackpool

Relegated: Hartlepool United and Leyton Orient

F.A. Cup 2016/2017

Round 1	Alfreton Town	1	Newport County	1	
Round 1	Blackpool	2	Kidderminster Harriers	0	
Round 1	Bolton Wanderers	1	Grimsby Town	0	
Round 1	Boreham Wood	2	Notts County	2	
Round 1	Bradford City	1	Accrington Stanley	2	
Round 1	Braintree Town	7	Eastbourne Borough	0	
Round 1	Bury	2	AFC Wimbledon	2	
Round 1	Cambridge United	1	Dover Athletic	1	
Round 1	Charlton Athletic	3	Scunthorpe United	1	
Round 1	Cheltenham Town	1	Crewe Alexandra	1	
Round 1	Colchester United	1	Chesterfield	2	
Round 1	Crawley Town	1	Bristol Rovers	1	
Round 1	Dagenham & Redbridge	0	FC Halifax Town	0	
Round 1	Dartford	3	Sutton United	6	
Round 1	Eastleigh	1	Swindon Town	1	
Round 1	Exeter City	1	Luton Town	3	
Round 1	Gillingham	2	Brackley Town	2	
Round 1	Hartlepool United	3	Stamford	0	
Round 1	Lincoln City	2	Altrincham	1	
Round 1	Maidstone United	1	Rochdale	1	
Round 1	Mansfield Town	1	Plymouth Argyle	2	
Round 1	Merstham	0	Oxford United	5	
Round 1	Millwall	1	Southend United	0	
Round 1	Milton Keynes Dons	3	Spennymoor Town	2	
Round 1	Morecambe	1	Coventry City	1	
Round 1	Northampton Town	6	Harrow Borough	0	
Round 1	Oldham Athletic	2	Doncaster Rovers	1	
Round 1	Peterborough United	2	Chesham United	1	
Round 1	Port Vale	1	Stevenage	0	
Round 1	Portsmouth	1	Wycombe Wanderers	2	
Round 1	Sheffield United	6	Leyton Orient	0	
Round 1	Shrewsbury Town	3	Barnet	0	
Round 1	Southport	0	Fleetwood Town	0	
Round 1	St Albans City	3	Carlisle United	5	
Round 1	Stockport County	2	Woking	4	
Round 1	Taunton Town	2	Barrow	2	
Round 1	Walsall	0	Macclesfield Town	1	
Round 1	Westfields	1	Curzon Ashton	1	
Round 1	Whitehawk	1	Stourbridge	1	
Round 1	Yeovil Town	2	Solihull Moors	2	
Replay	AFC Wimbledon	5	Bury	0	
Replay	Barrow	2	Taunton Town	1	
Replay	Brackley Town	4	Gillingham	3	(aet)
Replay	Bristol Rovers	4	Crawley Town	2	(aet)
Replay	Coventry City	2	Morecambe	1	
Replay	Crewe Alexandra	1	Cheltenham Town	4	
Replay	Curzon Ashton	3	Westfields	1	
Replay	Dover Athletic	2	Cambridge United	4	(aet)
Replay	FC Halifax Town	2	Dagenham & Redbridge	1	
Replay	Fleetwood Town	4	Southport	1	(aet)
Replay	Newport County	4	Alfreton Town	1	(aet)
Replay	Notts County	2	Boreham Wood	0	
Replay	Rochdale	2	Maidstone United	0	

Replay	Solihull Moors	1	Yeovil Town	1	(aet)
	Solihull Moors won 4-2 on penalties				
Replay	Stourbridge	3	Whitehawk	0	
Replay	Swindon Town	1	Eastleigh	3	
Round 2	Blackpool	1	Brackley Town	0	
Round 2	Bolton Wanderers	3	Sheffield United	2	
Round 2	Bristol Rovers	1	Barrow	2	
Round 2	Cambridge United	4	Coventry City	0	
Round 2	Carlisle United	0	Rochdale	2	
Round 2	Charlton Athletic	0	Milton Keynes Dons	0	
Round 2	Chesterfield	0	Wycombe Wanderers	5	
Round 2	Curzon Ashton	3	AFC Wimbledon	4	
Round 2	Eastleigh	3	FC Halifax Town	3	
Round 2	Lincoln City	3	Oldham Athletic	2	
Round 2	Luton Town	6	Solihull Moors	2	
Round 2	Macclesfield Town	0	Oxford United	0	
Round 2	Millwall	5	Braintree Town	2	
Round 2	Notts County	2	Peterborough United	2	
Round 2	Plymouth Argyle	0	Newport County	0	
Round 2	Port Vale	4	Hartlepool United	0	
Round 2	Shrewsbury Town	0	Fleetwood Town	0	
Round 2	Stourbridge	1	Northampton Town	0	
Round 2	Sutton United	2	Cheltenham Town	1	
Round 2	Woking	0	Accrington Stanley	3	
Replay	FC Halifax Town	0	Eastleigh	2	
Replay	Fleetwood Town	3	Shrewsbury Town	2	
Replay	Milton Keynes Dons	3	Charlton Athletic	1	(aet)
Replay	Newport County	0	Plymouth Argyle	1	(aet)
Replay	Oxford United	3	Macclesfield Town	0	
Replay	Peterborough United	2	Notts County	0	
Round 3	Accrington Stanley	2	Luton Town	1	
Round 3	Barrow	0	Rochdale	2	
Round 3	Birmingham City	1	Newcastle United	1	
Round 3	Blackpool	0	Barnsley	0	
Round 3	Bolton Wanderers	0	Crystal Palace	0	
Round 3	Brentford	5	Eastleigh	1	
Round 3	Brighton & Hove Albion	2	Milton Keynes Dons	0	
Round 3	Bristol City	0	Fleetwood Town	0	
Round 3	Cambridge United	1	Leeds United	2	
Round 3	Cardiff City	1	Fulham	2	
Round 3	Chelsea	4	Peterborough United	1	
Round 3	Everton	1	Leicester City	2	
Round 3	Huddersfield Town	4	Port Vale	0	
Round 3	Hull City	2	Swansea City	0	
Round 3	Ipswich Town	2	Lincoln City	2	
Round 3	Liverpool	0	Plymouth Argyle	0	
Round 3	Manchester United	4	Reading	0	
Round 3	Middlesbrough	3	Sheffield Wednesday	0	
Round 3	Millwall	3	AFC Bournemouth	0	
Round 3	Norwich City	2	Southampton	2	
Round 3	Preston North End	1	Arsenal	2	
Round 3	Queenís Park Rangers	1	Blackburn Rovers	2	
Round 3	Rotherham United	2	Oxford United	3	
Round 3	Stoke City	0	Wolverhampton Wanderers	2	

Round 3	Sunderland	0	Burnley	0	
Round 3	Sutton United	0	AFC Wimbledon	0	
Round 3	Tottenham Hotspur	2	Aston Villa	0	
Round 3	Watford	2	Burton Albion	0	
Round 3	West Bromwich Albion	1	Derby County	2	
Round 3	West Ham United	0	Manchester City	5	
Round 3	Wigan Athletic	2	Nottingham Forest	0	
Round 3	Wycombe Wanderers	2	Stourbridge	1	
Replay	AFC Wimbledon	1	Sutton United	3	
Replay	Barnsley	1	Blackpool	2	(aet)
Replay	Burnley	2	Sunderland	0	
Replay	Crystal Palace	2	Bolton Wanderers	1	
Replay	Fleetwood Town	0	Bristol City	1	
Replay	Lincoln City	1	Ipswich Town	0	
Replay	Newcastle United	3	Birmingham City	1	
Replay	Plymouth Argyle	0	Liverpool	1	
Replay	Southampton	1	Norwich City	0	
Round 4	Blackburn Rovers	2	Blackpool	0	
Round 4	Burnley	2	Bristol City	0	
Round 4	Chelsea	4	Brentford	0	
Round 4	Crystal Palace	0	Manchester City	3	
Round 4	Derby County	2	Leicester City	2	
Round 4	Fulham	4	Hull City	1	
Round 4	Lincoln City	3	Brighton & Hove Albion	1	
Round 4	Liverpool	1	Wolverhampton Wanderers	2	
Round 4	Manchester United	4	Wigan Athletic	0	
Round 4	Middlesbrough	1	Accrington Stanley	0	
Round 4	Millwall	1	Watford	0	
Round 4	Oxford United	3	Newcastle United	0	
Round 4	Rochdale	0	Huddersfield Town	4	
Round 4	Southampton	0	Arsenal	5	
Round 4	Sutton United	1	Leeds United	0	
Round 4	Tottenham Hotspur	4	Wycombe Wanderers	3	
Replay	Leicester City	3	Derby County	1	(aet)
Round 5	Blackburn Rovers	1	Manchester United	2	
Round 5	Burnley	0	Lincoln City	1	
Round 5	Fulham	0	Tottenham	3	
Round 5	Huddersfield Town	0	Manchester City	0	
Round 5	Middlesbrough	3	Oxford United	2	
Round 5	Millwall	1	Leicester City	0	
Round 5	Sutton United	0	Arsenal	2	
Round 5	Wolverhampton Wanderers	0	Chelsea	3	
Replay	Manchester City	5	Huddersfield Town	1	
Round 6	Arsenal	5	Lincoln City	0	
Round 6	Chelsea	1	Manchester United	0	
Round 6	Middlesbrough	0	Manchester City	2	
Round 6	Tottenham Hotspur	6	Millwall	0	
Semi-final	Arsenal	2	Manchester City	1	(aet)
Semi-final	Chelsea	4	Tottenham Hotspur	2	
FINAL	Arsenal	2	Chelsea	1	

English Football League Cup 2016/2017

Round	Home	Score	Away	Score	
Round 1	Accrington Stanley	0	Bradford City	0	(aet)
	Accrington Stanley won 11-10 on penalties				
Round 1	Barnet	0	Millwall	4	
Round 1	Barnsley	1	Northampton Town	2	(aet)
Round 1	Birmingham City	0	Oxford United	1	(aet)
Round 1	Blackpool	4	Bolton Wanderers	2	(aet)
Round 1	Brighton & Hove Albion	4	Colchester United	0	
Round 1	Bristol Rovers	1	Cardiff City	0	(aet)
Round 1	Burton Albion	3	Bury	2	(aet)
Round 1	Cambridge United	2	Sheffield Wednesday	1	(aet)
Round 1	Carlisle United	2	Port Vale	1	
Round 1	Cheltenham Town	1	Charlton Athletic	0	
Round 1	Coventry City	3	Portsmouth	2	(aet)
Round 1	Derby County	1	Grimsby Town	0	
Round 1	Doncaster Rovers	1	Nottingham Forest	2	
Round 1	Exeter City	1	Brentford	0	(aet)
Round 1	Fleetwood Town	2	Leeds United	2	(aet)
	Leeds United won 5-4 on penalties				
Round 1	Ipswich Town	0	Stevenage	1	
Round 1	Leyton Orient	2	Fulham	3	
Round 1	Luton Town	3	Aston Villa	1	
Round 1	Mansfield Town	1	Blackburn Rovers	3	
Round 1	Newport County	2	Milton Keynes Dons	3	
Round 1	Oldham Athletic	2	Wigan Athletic	1	
Round 1	Peterborough United	3	AFC Wimbledon	2	
Round 1	Preston North End	1	Hartlepool United	0	
Round 1	Queen's Park Rangers	2	Swindon Town	2	
Round 1	Reading	2	Plymouth Argyle	0	
Round 1	Rochdale	3	Chesterfield	1	
Round 1	Rotherham United	4	Morecambe	5	(aet)
Round 1	Scunthorpe United	2	Notts County	0	(aet)
Round 1	Sheffield United	1	Crewe Alexandra	2	(aet)
Round 1	Shrewsbury Town	2	Huddersfield Town	1	
Round 1	Southend United	1	Gillingham	3	
Round 1	Walsall	0	Yeovil Town	2	(aet)
Round 1	Wolverhampton Wanderers	2	Crawley Town	1	
Round 1	Wycombe Wanderers	0	Bristol City	1	
Round 2	Accrington Stanley	1	Burnley	0	(aet)
Round 2	Blackburn Rovers	4	Crewe Alexandra	3	
Round 2	Burton Albion	0	Liverpool	5	
Round 2	Chelsea	3	Bristol Rovers	2	
Round 2	Crystal Palace	2	Blackpool	0	
Round 2	Derby County	1	Carlisle United	1	(aet)
	Derby County won 14-13 on penalties				
Round 2	Everton	4	Yeovil Town	0	
Round 2	Exeter City	1	Hull City	3	
Round 2	Fulham	2	Middlesbrough	1	(aet)
Round 2	Luton Town	0	Leeds United	1	
Round 2	Millwall	1	Nottingham Forest	2	
Round 2	Morecambe	1	AFC Bournemouth	2	
Round 2	Newcastle United	2	Cheltenham Town	0	
Round 2	Northampton Town	2	West Bromwich Albion	2	(aet)
	Northampton Town won 4-3 on penalties				

Round 2	Norwich City	6	Coventry City	1	
Round 2	Oxford United	2	Brighton and Hove Albion	4	
Round 2	Peterborough United	1	Swansea City	3	
Round 2	Preston North End	2	Oldham Athletic	0	
Round 2	Queenís Park Rangers	2	Rochdale	1	
Round 2	Reading	2	Milton Keynes Dons	2	(aet)
	Reading won 4-2 on penalties				
Round 2	Scunthorpe United	1	Bristol City	2	(aet)
Round 2	Stevenage	0	Stoke City	4	
Round 2	Sunderland	1	Shrewsbury Town	0	
Round 2	Watford	1	Gillingham	2	(aet)
Round 2	Wolverhampton Wanderers	2	Cambridge United	1	
Round 3	AFC Bournemouth	2	Preston North End	3	(aet)
Round 3	Brighton & Hove Albion	1	Reading	2	
Round 3	Derby County	0	Liverpool	3	
Round 3	Everton	0	Norwich City	2	
Round 3	Fulham	1	Bristol City	2	
Round 3	Leeds United	1	Blackburn Rovers	0	
Round 3	Leicester City	2	Chelsea	4	(aet)
Round 3	Newcastle United	2	Wolverhampton Wanderers	0	
Round 3	Northampton Town	1	Manchester United	3	
Round 3	Nottingham Forest	0	Arsenal	4	
Round 3	Queenís Park Rangers	1	Sunderland	2	
Round 3	Southampton	2	Crystal Palace	0	
Round 3	Stoke City	1	Hull City	2	
Round 3	Swansea City	1	Manchester City	2	
Round 3	Tottenham Hotspur	5	Gillingham	0	
Round 3	West Ham United	1	Accrington Stanley	0	
Round 4	Arsenal	2	Reading	0	
Round 4	Bristol City	1	Hull City	2	
Round 4	Leeds United	2	Norwich City	2	(aet)
	Leeds United won 3-2 on penalties				
Round 4	Liverpool	2	Tottenham Hotspur	1	
Round 4	Manchester United	1	Manchester City	0	
Round 4	Newcastle United	6	Preston North End	0	
Round 4	Southampton	1	Sunderland	0	
Round 4	West Ham United	2	Chelsea	1	
Round 5	Arsenal	0	Southampton	2	
Round 5	Hull City	1	Newcastle United	1	(aet)
	Hull City won 3-1 on penalties				
Round 5	Liverpool	2	Leeds United	0	
Round 5	Manchester United	4	West Ham United	1	
Semi-Finals					
1st leg	Manchester United	2	Hull City	0	
1st leg	Southampton	1	Liverpool	0	
2nd leg	Hull City	2	Manchester United	1	
	Manchester United won 3-2 on aggregate				
2nd leg	Liverpool	0	Southampton	1	
	Southampton won 2-0 on aggregate				
FINAL	Manchester United	3	Southampton	2	

Cup Statistics courtesy of www.soccerdata.com

ENGLAND INTERNATIONAL LINE-UPS AND STATISTICS 2015

5th September 2015
v SAN MARINO (ECQ)   *Serravalle*

J. Hart	Manchester City
N. Clyne	Liverpool
J. Stones	Everton
P. Jagielka	Everton
L. Shaw	Manchester United
J. Milner	Liverpool (sub. F. Delph 58)
J. Shelvey	Newcastle United
A. Oxlade-Chamberlain	Arsenal (sub. T. Walcott 67)
R. Barkley	Everton
J. Vardy	Leicester City
W. Rooney	Manchester United (sub. H. Kane 59)

Result 6-0   Rooney (pen), Brolli (og), Barkley, Walcott 2, Kane

8th September 2015
v SWITZERLAND (ECQ)   *Wembley*

J. Hart	Manchester City
N. Clyne	Liverpool (sub. J. Stones 68)
G. Cahill	Chelsea
C. Smalling	Manchester United
L. Shaw	Liverpool
J. Milner	Liverpool
J. Shelvey	Swansea City (sub. H. Kane 57)
F. Delph	Manchester City (sub. R. Barkley 3)
A. Oxlade-Chamberlain	Arsenal
W. Rooney	Manchester United
R. Sterling	Manchester City

Result 2-0   Kane, Rooney (pen)

9th October 2015
v ESTONIA (ECQ)   *Wembley*

J. Hart	Manchester City
N. Clyne	Liverpool
G. Cahill	Chelsea
C. Smalling	Manchester United
R. Bertrand	Southampton
J. Milner	Liverpool
R. Barkley	Everton (sub. D. Alli 88)
T. Walcott	Arsenal (sub. J. Vardy 83)
A. Lallana	Liverpool (sub. A. Oxlade-Chamberlain 73)
R. Sterling	Manchester City
H. Kane	Tottenham Hotspur

Result 2-0   Walcott, Sterling

12th October 2015
v LITHUANIA (ECQ)   *Vilnius*

J. Butland	Stoke City
K. Walker	Tottenham Hotspur
P. Jones	Manchester United
P. Jagielka	Everton
K. Gibbs	Arsenal
J. Shelvey	Swansea City
A. Oxlade-Chamberlain	Arsenal
A. Lallana	Liverpool (sub. D. Alli 67)
R. Barkley	Everton (sub. A. Townsend 73)
J. Vardy	Leicester City
H. Kane	Tottenham Hotspur (sub. D. Ings 59)

Result 3-0   Barkley, Arlauskis (og), Oxlade-Chamberlain

13th November 2015
v SPAIN   *Alicante*

J. Hart	Manchester City
K. Walker	Tottenham Hotspur
P. Jones	Manchester United
C. Smalling	Manchester United (sub. G. Cahill 84)
R. Bertrand	Southampton
M. Carrick	Man. United (sub. J. Shelvey 90+1)
F. Delph	Manchester City (sub. E. Dier 63)
A. Lallana	Liverpool (sub. D. Alli 63)
R. Barkley	Everton (sub. W. Rooney 73)
R. Sterling	Manchester City
H. Kane	Tottenham Hotspur

Result 0-2

17th November 2015
v FRANCE   *Wembley*

J. Hart	Manchester City (sub. J. Butland 45)
N. Clyne	Liverpool
J. Stones	Everton
G. Cahill	Chelsea
K. Gibbs	Arsenal
D. Alli	Tottenham Hotspur (sub. P. Jones 88)
E. Dier	Tottenham Hotspur
R. Sterling	Manchester City (sub. A. Lallana 68)
R. Barkley	Everton (sub. J. Shelvey 79)
W. Rooney	Manchester United
H. Kane	Tottenham Hot. (sub. R. Bertrand 80)

Result 2-0   Alli, Rooney

ENGLAND INTERNATIONAL LINE-UPS AND STATISTICS 2016

26th March 2016
v GERMANY *Berlin*

J. Butland	Stoke City (sub. F. Forster 45+1)
N. Clyne	Liverpool
G. Cahill	Chelsea
C. Smalling	Manchester United
D. Rose	Tottenham Hotspur
E. Dier	Tottenham Hotspur
J. Henderson	Liverpool
A. Lallana	Liverpool (sub. R. Barkley 71)
D. Alli	Tottenham Hotspur
D. Welbeck	Arsenal (sub. J. Vardy 71)
H. Kane	Tottenham Hotspur

Result 3-2 Kane, Vardy, Dier

29th March 2016
v NETHERLANDS *Wembley*

F. Forster	Southampton
K. Walker	Tottenham Hotspur
C. Smalling	Man. United (sub. P. Jagielka 70)
J. Stones	Everton
D. Rose	Tottenham Hotspur (sub. N. Clyne 58)
D. Drinkwater	Leicester City (sub. E. Dier 85)
J. Milner	Liverpool (sub. D. Alli 82)
A. Lallana	Liverpool (sub. H. Kane 70)
R. Barkley	Everton
J. Vardy	Leicester City
D. Sturridge	Liverpool (sub. T. Walcott 58)

Result 1-2 Vardy

22nd May 2016
v TURKEY *Etihad, Manchester*

J. Hart	Manchester City
K. Walker	Tottenham Hotspur
G. Cahill	Chelsea
J. Stones	Everton
D. Rose	Tottenham Hotspur
D. Alli	Tottenham Hotspur
E. Dier	Tottenham Hotspur
J. Wilshere	Arsenal (sub. J. Henderson 66)
R. Sterling	Man. City (sub. D. Drinkwater 73)
H. Kane	Tottenham Hotspur
J. Vardy	Leicester City

Result 2-1 Kane, Vardy

27th May 2016
v AUSTRALIA *Sunderland*

F. Forster	Southampton (sub. T. Heaton 87)
N. Clyne	Liverpool
C. Smalling	Manchester United (sub. E. Dier 73)
J. Stones	Everton
R. Bertrand	Southampton
J. Wilshere	Arsenal (sub. J. Milner 45)
J. Henderson	Liverpool
D. Drinkwater	Leicester City
A. Lallana	Liverpool (sub. W. Rooney 45)
R. Sterling	Man. City (sub. A. Townsend 76)
M.Rashford	Man. United (sub. R. Barkley 63)

Result 2-1 Rashford, Rooney

2nd June 2016
v PORTUGAL *Wembley*

J. Hart	Manchester City
K. Walker	Tottenham Hotspur
G. Cahill	Chelsea
C. Smalling	Manchester United
D. Rose	Tottenham Hotspur
J. Milner	Liverpool (sub. J. Wilshire 66)
E. Dier	Tottenham Hotspur
D. Alli	Tott. Hostpur (sub. J. Henderson 90)
H. Kane	Tott. Hotspur (sub. D. Sturridge 78)
W. Rooney	Man. United (sub. A. Lallana 78)
J. Vardy	Leicester City (sub. R. Sterling 66)

Result 1-0 Smalling

11th June 2016
v RUSSIA (ECF) *Marseille*

J. Hart	Manchester City
K. Walker	Tottenham Hotspur
G. Cahill	Chelsea
C. Smalling	Manchester United
D. Rose	Tottenham Hotspur
D. Alli	Tottenham Hotspur
E. Dier	Tottenham Hotspur
W. Rooney	Man. United (sub. J. Wilshire 78)
A. Lallana	Liverpool
H. Kane	Tottenham Hotspur
R. Sterling	Manchester City (sub. J. Milner 87)

Result 1-1 Dier

ENGLAND INTERNATIONAL LINE-UPS AND STATISTICS 2016

16th June 2016
v WALES (ECF)   *Lens*
J. Hart	Manchester City
K. Walker	Tottenham Hotspur
G. Cahill	Chelsea
C. Smalling	Manchester United
D. Rose	Tottenham Hotspur
D. Alli	Tottenham Hotspur
E. Dier	Tottenham Hotspur
W. Rooney	Manchester United
A. Lallana	Liverpool (sub. M. Rashford 73)
H. Kane	Tottenham Hotspur (sub. J. Vardy 45)
R. Sterling	Man. City (sub. D. Sturridge 45)

Result 2-1   Vardy, Sturridge

20th June 2016
v SLOVAKIA (ECF)   *Saint-Étienne*
J. Hart	Manchester City
N. Clyne	Liverpool
G. Cahill	Chelsea
C. Smalling	Manchester United
R. Bertrand	Southampton
J. Henderson	Liverpool
E. Dier	Tottenham Hotspur
J. Wilshere	Arsenal (sub. W. Rooney 56)
D. Sturridge	Liverpool (sub. H. Kane 76)
J. Vardy	Leicester City
A. Lallana	Liverpool (sub. D. Alli 60)

Result 0-0

27th June 2016
v ICELAND (ECF)   *Nice*
J. Hart	Manchester City
K. Walker	Tottenham Hotspur
G. Cahill	Chelsea
C. Smalling	Manchester City
D. Rose	Tottenham Hotspur
D. Alli	Tottenham Hotspur
E. Dier	Tott. Hotspur (sub. J. Wilshire 45)
W. Rooney	Man. United (sub. M. Rashford 86)
D. Sturridge	Liverpool
H. Kane	Tottenham Hotspur
R. Sterling	Manchester City (sub. J. Vardy 60)

Result 1-2   Rooney (pen)

4th September 2016
v SLOVAKIA (WCQ)   *Trnava*
J. Hart	Torino
K. Walker	Tottenham Hotspur
G. Cahill	Chelsea
J. Stones	Manchester City
D. Rose	Tottenham Hotspur
J. Henderson	Liverpool (sub. D. Alli 64)
E. Dier	Tottenham Hotspur
W. Rooney	Manchester United
R. Sterling	Manchester City (sub. T. Walcott 71)
H. Kane	Tott. Hotspur (sub. D. Sturridge 82)
A. Lallana	Liverpool

Result 1-0   Lallana

8th October 2016
v MALTA (WCQ)   *Wembley*
J. Hart	Torino
K. Walker	Tottenham Hotspur
G. Cahill	Chelsea
J. Stones	Manchester City
R. Bertrand	Southampton (sub. D. Rose 19)
D. Alli	Tottenham Hotspur
J. Henderson	Liverpool
W. Rooney	Manchester United
T. Walcott	Arsenal (sub. M. Rashford 68)
D. Sturridge	Liverpool (sub. J. Vardy 73)
J. Lingard	Manchester United

Result 2-0   Sturridge, Alli

11th October 2016
v SLOVENIA (WCQ)   *Ljubljana*
J. Hart	Torino
K. Walker	Tottenham Hotspur
G. Cahill	Chelsea
J. Stones	Manchester City
D. Rose	Tottenham Hotspur
J. Henderson	Liverpool
E. Dier	Tottenham Hotspur
T. Walcott	Arsenal (sub. A. Townsend 62)
D. Alli	Tott. Hotspur (sub. W. Rooney 73)
J. Lingard	Manchester United
D. Sturridge	Liverpool (sub. M. Rashford 82)

Result 0-0

ENGLAND INTERNATIONAL LINE-UPS AND STATISTICS 2016-2017

11th November 2016
v SCOTLAND (WCQ)   *Wembley*

J. Hart	Torino
K. Walker	Tottenham Hotspur
G. Cahill	Chelsea
J. Stones	Manchester City
D. Rose	Tottenham Hotspur
J. Henderson	Liverpool
E. Dier	Tottenham Hotspur
R. Sterling	Manchester City
W. Rooney	Manchester United
A. Lallana	Liverpool
D. Sturridge	Liverpool

Result 3-0   Sturridge, Lallana, Cahill

15th November 2016
v SPAIN   *Wembley*

J. Hart	Torino (sub. T. Heaton 45)
N. Clyne	Liverpool
G. Cahill	Chelsea (sub. P. Jagielka 45)
J. Stones	Manchester City
D. Rose	Tott. Hotspur (sub. A. Cresswell 79)
J. Henderson	Liverpool
E. Dier	Tottenham Hotspur
R. Sterling	Man. City (sub. A. Townsend 65)
A. Lallana	Liverpool (sub. T. Walcott 27)
J. Lingard	Manchester United
J. Vardy	Leicester City (sub. M. Rashford 67)

Result 2-2   Lallana (pen), Vardy

22nd March 2017
v GERMANY   *Dortmund*

J. Hart	Torino
M. Keane	Burnley
C. Smalling	Man. United (sub. J. Stones 84)
G. Cahill	Chelsea
K. Walker	Tottenham Hotspur
J. Livermore	West Brom. (sub. J. Ward-Prowse 83)
E. Dier	Tottenham Hotspur
R. Bertrand	Southampton (sub. L. Shaw 83)
A. Lallana	Liverpool (sub. N. Redmond 66)
D. Alli	Tott. Hotspur (sub. J. Lingard 71)
J. Vardy	Leicester City (sub. M. Rashford 70)

Result 0-1

26th March 2017
v LITHUANIA (WCQ)   *Wembley*

J. Hart	Manchester City
K. Walker	Tottenham Hotspur
J. Stones	Manchester City
M. Keane	Burnley
R. Bertrand	Southampton
A. Oxlade-Chamberlain	Arsenal
E. Dier	Tottenham Hotspur
A. Lallana	Liverpool
D. Alli	Tottenham Hotspur
R. Sterling	Liverpool (sub. M. Rashford 60)
J. Defoe	Sunderland (sub. J. Vardy 60)

Result 2-0   Defoe, Vardy

10th June 2017
v SCOTLAND (WCQ)   *Hampden Park*

J. Hart	Manchester City
K. Walker	Tottenham Hotspur
C. Smalling	Manchester United
G. Cahill	Chelsea
R. Bertrand	Southampton
J. Livermore	West Brom. (sub. J. Defoe 90+2)
E. Dier	Tottenham Hotspur
M. Rashford	Manchester United (sub. A. Oxlade-Chamberlain 65)
D. Alli	Tott. Hotspur (sub. R. Sterling 84)
A. Lallana	Liverpool
H. Kane	Tottenham Hotspur

Result 2-2   Oxlade-Chamberlain, Kane

13th June 2017
v FRANCE   *Paris*

T. Heaton	Burnley (sub. J. Butland 45)
P. Jones	Man. United (sub. A. Cresswell 82)
J. Stones	Manchester City
G. Cahill	Chelsea
K. Trippier	Tott. Hotspur (sub. A. Lallana 76)
A. Oxlade-Chamberlain	Arsenal
E. Dier	Tottenham Hotspur
R. Bertrand	Southampton (sub. K. Walker 45)
R. Sterling	Manchester City
D. Alli	Tottenham Hotspur
H. Kane	Tottenham Hotspur

Result 2-3   Kane 2 (1 pen)

Supporters' Guides and Tables books

Our Supporters' Guide series has been published since 1982 and the new 2018 editions contain the 2016/2017 Season's results and tables, Directions, Photographs, Telephone numbers, Parking information, Admission details, Disabled information and much more.

Our Football Tables books are perfect companions to the Supporters' Guides and contain historical Football League, Non-League and Scottish final tables up to the end of the 2016/2017 season.

THE SUPPORTERS' GUIDE TO PREMIER & FOOTBALL LEAGUE CLUBS 2018

This 34th edition covers all 92 Premiership and Football League clubs. *Price £9.99*

NON-LEAGUE SUPPORTERS' GUIDE AND YEARBOOK 2018

This 26th edition covers all 68 clubs in Step 1 & Step 2 of Non-League football – the Vanarama National League, National League North and National League South. *Price £9.99*

SCOTTISH FOOTBALL SUPPORTERS' GUIDE AND YEARBOOK 2018

The 25th edition featuring all Scottish Professional Football League, Highland League and Lowland League clubs. *Price £9.99*

ENGLISH FOOTBALL LEAGUE & F.A. PREMIER LEAGUE TABLES 1888-2017

The 20th edition contains every Football League & F.A. Premier League final table plus play-off results and F.A. Cup and League Cup semi-final & final results. *Price £9.99*

NON-LEAGUE FOOTBALL TABLES 1889-2017

The 15th edition contains final league tables for the National League (formerly the Football Conference) and its 3 feeder leagues, the Northern Premier League, Southern League and Isthmian League. This edition also contains tables for the Combined Counties League 1922-2017 plus, for the first time, historical notes about the National League and Northern Premier League. *Price £9.99*

SCOTTISH FOOTBALL TABLES 1890-2017

The 6th edition contains final league tables for all Scottish Professional Football League, Scottish League, Scottish Premier League, Highland League and Lowland Football League seasons. *Price £9.99*

These books are available UK & Surface post free from –

Soccer Books Limited (Dept. SBL)
72 St. Peter's Avenue
Cleethorpes, DN35 8HU
United Kingdom